D1074174

WOODLAND TALES

WOODLAND TALES

BY

ERNEST THOMPSON SETON

WITH 100 DRAWINGS
BY
THE AUTHOR

AUTHOR OF "WILD ANIMALS AT HOME," "WILD ANIMALS I HAVE KNOWN," "TWO LITTLE SAVAGES," "BIOGRAPHY OF A GRIZZLY," "LIFE HISTORIES OF NORTHERN ANIMALS," "ROLF IN THE WOODS," "THE BOOK OF WOODCRAFT." CHIEF OF THE WOODCRAFT LEAGUE OF AMERICA

GARDEN CITY NEW YORK
DOUBLEDAY, DORAN & COMPANY, INC.
1929

C
PRINTED IN THE UNITED STATES
AT
THE COUNTRY LIFE PRESS, GARDEN CITY, N. Y.

PREFACE

To the Guide

THESE Mother Carey Tales were written for children of all ages, who have not outgrown the delight of a fairy tale. It might almost be said that they were written chiefly for myself, for I not only have had the pleasure of telling them to the little ones, and enjoying their quick response, but have also had the greater pleasure of thinking them and setting them down.

As I write, I look from a loved window, across a landscape that I love, and my eye rests on a tall beautiful pine planted with my own hands years ago. It is a mass of green fringes, with gem-like tips of buds and baby cones, beautiful, exquisitely beautiful, whether seen from afar as a green spire, or viewed close at hand as jewellery. It is beautiful, fragile and—unimportant, as the world sees it; yet through its wind-waved mass one can get little glimpses of the thing that backs it all, the storm-defying shaft, the enduring rigid living growing trunk of massive timber that gives it the nobility of strength, and adds value to the rest; sometimes it must be sought for, but it always surely is there, ennobling the lesser pretty things.

I hope this tree is a fair image of my fairy tale. I know my child friends will love the piney fringes and the jewel cones, and they can find the unyielding timber in its underlying truth, if they seek for it. If they do not, it is enough to have them love the cones.

All are not fairy tales. Other chapters set forth things to see, thing to do, things to go to, things to know, things to remember. These, sanctified in the blue outdoors, spell "Woodcraft," the one pursuit of man that never dies or palls, the thing that in the bygone ages gifted him and yet again will gift him with the seeing eye, the thinking hand, the body that fails not, the winged soul that stores up precious memories.

It is hoped that these chapters will show how easy and alluring, and how good a thing it is.

While they are meant for the children six years of age and upward, it is assumed that Mother (or Father) will be active as a leader; therefore it is addressed, first of all, to the parent, whom throughout we shall call the "Guide."

Some of these stories date back to my school days, although the first actually published was "Why the Chicadee Goes Crazy Twice a Year." This in its original form appeared in "Our Animal Friends" in September, 1893. Others, as "The Fingerboard Goldenrod," "Brook-Brownie," "The Bluebird," "Diablo and the Dogwood," "How the Violets Came," "How the Indian Summer Came," "The Twin Stars," "The Fairy Lamps," "How the Littlest Owl Came," "How the Shad Came," appeared in slightly different form in the *Century Magazine*, 1903 and 1904.

My thanks are due to the Authorities of the American Museum who have helped me with specimens and criticism; to the published writings of Dr. W. J. Holland and Clarence M. Weed for guidance in insect problems; to Britton and Browne's "Illustrated Flora, U. S. and Canada"; and to the Nature Library of Doubleday, Page & Co., for light in matters botanic; to Mrs. Daphne Drake and Mrs. Mary S. Dominick for many valuable suggestions, and to my wife,

Grace Gallatin Seton, for help with the purely literary work.

Also to Oliver P. Medsger, the naturalist of Lincoln High School, Jersey City, N. J., for reading with critical care those parts of the manuscript that deal with flowers and insects, as well as for the ballad of the Ox-eye, the story of its coming to America, and the photograph of the Mechameck.

CONTENTS

Things to See in Springtime

The Seeing Eye

Things to See in Summertime

Things to See in Autumntime

Things to See in Wintertime

Things to Know

The Story of The Trail

Things to Do

The Thinking Hand

Things to Remember

The Winged Soul that Stores up Precious Memories.

INTRODUCTION

Mother Carey

All-mother! Mater Cara! I have never seen you, but I hungered so to know you that I understood it when you came, unseen, and silently whispered to me that first time in the long ago.

I cannot tell the children what you look like, Mother Carey, for mortal eye hath never rested on your face; and yet I can offer them a portrait, O strong Angel of the Wild Things, neither young nor old—Oh! loving One that neither trembles nor relents!

A mink he was, a young mink and foolish. One of a happy brood, who were seeing the world with their mother —a first glimpse of it. She was anxious and leading, happy and proud, warning, sniffing, inviting, loving, yet angersome at trivial disobedience, doling out her wisdom in nips and examples and shrill warnings that all heeded; except this one, the clever fool of the family, the self-satisfied smart one. He would not be warned, the thing smelt so good. He plunged ahead. Mother was a fool; he was wiser than Mother. Here was a merry feasting for him. Then *clank!* The iron jaws of a trap sprang from the hiding grass, and clutched on his soft young paws. Screams of pain, futile strainings, writhings, ragings and moanings; bloody jaws on the trap; the mother distraught with grief, eager to take all the punishment herself, but helpless and stunned, unable to leave; the little brothers, aghast at this first touch of passion, this glimpse of reality, skurrying, scared, going and coming, mesmerized, with glowing eyes and bristling shoulder-fur. And the mother, mad with sorrow, goaded by the screaming, green-eyed, vacant-minded, despairing—till a new spirit entered into her, the spirit of Cara the All-mother, Mother Carey the Beneficent, Mother Carey the wise Straightwalker. Then the mother mink, inspired, sprang on her suffering baby. With all the power of her limbs she sprang and clutched; with all the power of her love she craunched. His screams were ended; his days in the land were ended. He had not heeded her wisdom; the family fool was finished. The race was better, better for the suffering fool mink; better for the suffering mother mink.

The spirit left her; left her limp and broken-hearted. And away on the wind went riding, grimly riding her empire.

Four swift steeds for riding, has she, the White Wind, the West Wind, the Wet Wind and the Waking Wind. But mostly she rides the swift West Wind.

She is strong, is Mother Carey, strong, wise, inexorable, calm and direct as an iceberg. And beneficent; but she loves the strong ones best. She ever favours the wise ones. She is building, ceaselessly building. The good brick she sets in a place of honour, and the poor one she grinds into gravel for the workmen to walk on.

She loves you, but far less than she does your race. It may be that you are not wise, and if it seem best, she will drop a tear and crush you into the dust.

Three others there be of power, like Mother Carey: Maka Ina who is Mother Earth; El Sol, the Sun in the Sky, and Diablo the Evil Spirit of Disease and Dread. But over all is the One Great Spirit, the Beginning and the Ruler with these and many messengers, who do His bidding. But mostly you shall hear of Mother Carey.

It is long ago since first I heard her whisper, and though I hear better now than then, I have no happier memory than that earliest message.

"Ho Wayseeker," she called, "I have watched your struggle to find the pathway, and I know that you will love the things that belong to it. Therefore, I will show you the trail, and this is what it will lead you to: a thousand pleasant friendships that will offer honey in little thorny cups, the twelve secrets of the underbrush, the health of sunlight, suppleness of body, the unafraidness of the night, the delight of deep water, the goodness of rain, the story of the trail, the knowledge of the swamp, the aloofness of knowing,—yea, more, a crown and a little kingdom measured to your power and all your own.

"But there is a condition attached. When you have found a trail you are thereby ordained a guide. When you have won a kingdom you must give it to the world or lose it. For those who have got power must with it bear responsibility; evade the one, the other fades away."

This is the pledge I am trying to keep; I want to be your Guide. I am offering you my little kingdom.

THINGS TO SEE IN SPRINGTIME

Blue-eyes the Snow Child

Things to See in Springtime

TALE 1

Blue-eyes, the Snow Child, or The Story of Hepatica

HAVE you ever seen El Sol, the Chief of the Wonder-workers, brother to Mother Carey? Yes, you have, though probably you did not know it; at least you could not look him in the face. Well, I am going to tell you about him, and tell of a sad thing that happened to him, and to some one whom he loved more than words can tell.

Tall and of blazing beauty was El Sol, the King of the Wonder-workers; his hair was like shining gold, and stood straight out a yard from his head, as he marched over the hilltops.

Everyone loved him, except a very few, who once had dared to fight him, and had been worsted. Everyone else loved him, and he liked everybody, without really loving them. Until one day, as he walked in his garden, he suddenly came on a beautiful white maiden, whom he had never seen before. Her eyes were of the loveliest blue, her hair was so soft that it floated on the air, and her robe was white, covered with ferns done in white lace.

He fell deeply in love with her at once, but she waved a warning hand, when he tried to come near.

"Who are you, oh radiant princess? I love you even before I hear you speak."

"I am Snowroba, the daughter of the great King Jack-frost," she said.

"I love you as I never loved any one. Will you marry me? I am the King of the Wonder-workers. I will make you the Queen."

"No," said she, "I cannot marry you, for it is written that if one of my people marry one of your people, she will sink down and die in a day."

Then El Sol was very sad. But he said, "May I not see you again?"

"Yes," she answered, "I will meet you here in the morning, for it is pleasant to look on your beauty," and her voice tinkled sweetly.

So she met him in the morning, and again on the third morning. He loved her madly now, and though she held back, he seized her in his arms and kissed her tenderly.

Then her arms fell weakly to her sides, and her eyes half closed as she said: "I know now that the old writing spake truth. I love you, I love you, my love; but you have killed me."

And she sank down, a limp white form, on the leafy ground.

El Sol was wild with grief. He tried to revive her, to bring her back.

She only whispered, "Good-bye, my love. I am going fast. You will see me no more, but come to this place a year from now. It may be Maka Ina will be kind, and will send you a little one that is yours and mine."

Her white body melted away, as he bent over it and wept.

He came back every morning, but saw Snowroba no more. One year from that day, as he lingered sadly over the sacred spot, he saw a new and wonderful flower come forth. Its bloom was of the tenderest violet blue, and it was full of expression. As he gazed, he saw those eyes again; the scalding tears dropped from his eyes, and burned its leaves into a blotched and brownish colour. He remembered, and understood her promise now. He knew that this was their blue-eyed little one.

In the early springtime we can see it. Three sunny days on the edge of the snowdrift will bring it forth. The hunterfolk who find it, say that it is just one of the spring flowers, out earlier than any other, and is called Liverleaf, but we Woodcrafters know better. We know it is Hepatica, the child of El Sol and Snowroba.

TALE 2

The Story of the White Dawnsinger or How the Bloodroot Came

HAVE you noticed that there are no snow-white birds in our woods during summer? Mother Carey long ago made it a rule that all snow-white landbirds should go north, when the snow was gone in the springtime. And they were quite obedient; they flew, keeping just on the south edge of the melting snow.

But it so happened that one of the sweetest singers of all—the snow-white Dawnsinger with the golden bill and the ruby legs—was flying northward with his bride, when she sprained her wing so she could not fly at all.

There was no other help for it; they must stay in that thicket till her wing grew strong again.

The other white birds flew on, but the Dawnsinger waited. He sang his merriest songs to cheer her. He brought her food: and he warned her when enemies were near.

A moon had come and gone. Now she was well again, and strong on the wing. He was anxious to go on to their northern home. A second warning came from Mother Carey, "White birds go north."

But the sunny woodside had become very pleasant, food was abundant, and the little white lady said, "Why should we go north when it is so much nicer right here?"

The Dawnsinger felt the same way, and the next time the warning came, "White birds go north," he would not listen at all, and they settled down to a joyful life in the woods.

They did not know anything about the Yellow-eyed Whizz. They never would have known, had they gone north at their right time. But the Yellow-eyed Whizz was coming. It came, and It always goes straight after white things in the woods, for brown things It cannot see.

Dawnsinger was high on a tree, praising the light in a glorious song, that he had just made up, when It singled him out by his whiteness, and pierced him through.

He fell fluttering and dying; and as she flew to him, with a cry of distress, the Yellow-eyed wicked Whizz struck her down by his side.

The Chewinks scratched leaves over the two white bodies, and—I think—that Mother Carey dropped a tear on the place.

That was the end of the White Dawnsinger and his bride. Yet every year, at that same place, as the snow goes, the brown leaves move and part, and up from beneath there comes a beautiful white flower.

Its bloom threads are yellow like the Dawnsinger's beak, and its stem is ruby like his legs; all the rest is snow-white like his plumes. It rises, looks about, faces the sun, and sings a little odour-song, a little aroma-iay. If you look deep down into the open soul of the Dawnsinger you will see the little golden thoughts he sings about. Then up from the same grave comes another, just the same, but a little smaller, and for a while they stand up side by side, and

The Story of the White Dawnsinger

praise the light. But the Wither-bloom that haunts the flowers as the Yellow-eyed Whizz does the birds, soon finds them out; their song is ended, their white plumes are scattered, and they shrink back into their grave, to be side by side again.

You can find their little bodies, but deal gently with them, for they are wounded; you may make them bleed again.

And when you hear the Chewinks scratching in the underbrush, remember they are putting leaves on the grave of the White Dawnsinger.

Surely you have guessed the secret; the flower is the Bloodroot, and the Whizz is the Sharp-shinned Hawk.

TALE 3

The Prairie-girl with Yellow Hair

TALL and fair was the Prairie-girl. She was not very pretty, but her form was slender and graceful, and her head was covered with a mass of golden hair that made you see her from afar off. It has been whispered that she was deeply in love with El Sol, for wherever he went, she turned her head to look at him; and when she could not see him, she drooped and languished. But he never seemed to notice her. As she grew older her golden head turned white, and at last the swish of Mother Carey's horses carried away all her white hair, and left her old, bald, and ugly. So she pined and died, and Maka Ina buried her poor little body under the grass. But some say it was Father Time that blew her hair away, and that El Sol had the body cremated.

If you look on the lawns or the fields in springtime, you are sure to find the Prairie-girl. The Guide can show her to

The Prairie-girl

you, if you do not know her. But he will call her "Common Dandelion," and I do not know of any flower that has so many things for us children to remember.

If you are learning French, you will see how it got the name "Dandelion"; it used to be written *dent de lion;* that is, "tooth of a lion"; because its leaves are edged with sharp teeth, like a lion's jaw.

Its golden-yellow flower is said to open when the Swallows arrive from the south, that is, in April; and though it blooms chiefly in springtime it keeps on blooming till long after the Swallows fly away. It certainly thrives as long as the sun shines on it, and fades when the cold dark season comes. But I have seen it out in November; that is, the Dandelion blooms for fully nine months. I do not know of any other flower that does; most of them are done in one month.

When the yellow flower is over, its place is taken by a beautiful globe of soft, white plumes; this is why the story says its golden hair turns white with age. The children believe that this woolly head will tell you the time of day. You hold it up, then pretend you are Father Time blowing her hair away, blow a sharp puff with your breath, then another and another, till the plumes are blown away. If it takes four blows, they say it means four o'clock; but it is not a very true clock.

Some children make a wish, then blow once and say, "this year"; the second time, "next year"; the third time, "some time"; the fourth time, "never." Then begin all over, and keep on as long as any plumes are left, to tell when the wish is coming true.

Now pull the head off the stalk. You will find it leaves a long, open tube that sounds like a trumpet when you blow through it from the small end. If you force your finger into the big end, and keep pushing, you split the tube into two or three pieces; put these in your mouth and they will curl up like ringlets. Some children hang these on their ears for ornaments. Take a stalk for each year of your age; pull its head off. Then you will find that the top end will go into the bottom and make a ring. Use all the stalks you have gathered, to make a chain; now throw this chain into a low tree. If it sticks the first time, your wish will come true this year. Each time it falls puts your wish a year farther away.

This may not be true; but it is a game to play. Some big girls use it, to find out when they are going to be married.

Now dig up the whole plant, root and all—the gardener will be much obliged to you for doing so—take it home, and ask the Guide to make the leaves into a salad; you will find it good to eat; most Europeans eat it regularly, either raw, or boiled as greens.

Last of all, ask the Guide to roast the root, till it is brown and crisp, then grind it in a coffee-mill, and use it to make coffee. Some people think it better than real coffee; at any rate, the doctors say it is much healthier, for it is nourishing food, and does not do one any harm at all. But perhaps you will not like it. You may think all the time you are eating the body of the poor little Prairie-girl, who died of love.

TALE 4

The Cat's-eye Toad, a Child of Maka Ina

WHEN you were little, O Guide! didn't you delight in the tales of gnomes or *nibelungen*, those strange underground creatures that lived hidden from the light, and busied themselves with precious stones and metals? How unwillingly we gave up those glad beliefs, as we inevitably grew old and lost our fairyland eyes!

The Cat's eye Toad (life size)

But you must not give up all your joyful creeds; you must keep on believing in the weird underground dwarfs; for I am going to tell you of one that the cold calculating Professor Science has at last accepted, and that lives in your own back-yard. That is, the Cat's-eye Toad or Spadefoot. It is much like a common Toad, but a little smoother, the digging spade on its hind foot is bigger and its eye, its beautiful gold-stone eye, has the pupil up and down like that of a Cat, instead of level as in its cousin, the warty Hoptoad.

But the wonderful thing about the Cat's-eye is that it spends most of its life underground, coming out in the early springtime for a few days of the most riotous honeymoon in some small pond, where it sings a loud chorus till mated, lays a few hundred eggs, to be hatched into tadpoles, then backs itself into its underground world by means of the boring machine on its hind feet, to be heard no more that season, and seen no more, unless some one chance to dig it out, just as Hans in the story dug out the mole-gnome.

In the fairy tale the Shepherd-boy was rewarded by the gnome for digging him out; for he received both gold and precious stones. But our gnome does not wish us to dig him out; nevertheless, if you do, you will be rewarded with a golden fact, and a glimpse of two wonderful jewel eyes.

According to one who knows him well, the Cat's-eye buries itself far underground, and sleeps days, or weeks, *perhaps years* at a time. Once a grave-digger found a Cat's-eye three feet two inches down in the earth with no way out.

How and when are we then to find this strange creature? Only during his noisy honeymoon in April.

Do you know the soft trilling whistle of the common Hoptoad in May? The call of the Cat's-eye is of the same style but very loud and harsh, and heard early in April. If on some warm night in springtime, you hear a song which sounds like a cross between a Toad's whistle and a Chicken's squawk, get a searchlight and go quietly to the place. The light will help you to come close, and in the water up to his chin, you will see him, his gold-stone eyes blazing like jewels and his throat blown out like a mammoth pearl, each time he utters the "squawk" which he intends for a song. And it *is* a song, and a very successful one, for a visit to the same pond a week or two later, will show you—not the Cat's-eye or his mate, they have gone a-tunnelling—but a swarm of little black pin-like tadpole Cat's-eyes, born and bred in the glorious sunlight but doomed and ready, if they live, to follow in their parents' tracks far underground. Sure proof that the song did win a mate, and was crowned with the success for which all woodland, and marshland song first was made.

TALE 5

How the Bluebird Came

NANA-BO-JOU, that some think is the Indian name for El Sol and some say is Mother Carey, was sleeping his winter's sleep in the big island just above the thunder-dam that men call Niagara. Four moons had waned, but still he slept. The frost draperies of his couch were gone; his white blanket was burnt into holes. He turned over a little; then the ice on the river cracked like near-by thunder. When he turned again, it began to slip over the big beaver-dam of Niagara, but still he did not awake.

The great Er-Beaver in his pond, that men call Lake Erie, flapped his tail, and the waves rolled away to the shore, and set the ice heaving, cracking, and groaning; but Nana-bo-jou slept on.

Then the Ice-demons pounded the shore of the island with their clubs. They pushed back the whole river-flood till

How the Bluebird Came

the channel was dry, then let it rush down like the end of all things, and they shouted together:

"Nana-bo-jou! Nana-bo-jou! Nana-bo-jou! Wake up!"

But still he slept calmly on.

Then came a soft, sweet voice, more gentle than the mating turtle of Miami. It was in the air, but it was nowhere, and yet it was in the trees, in the water, and it was in Nana-bo-jou too. He felt it, and it awoke him. He sat up and looked about. His white blanket was gone; only a few tatters of it were to be seen in the shady places. In the sunny spots the shreds of the fringe with its beads had taken root and were growing into little flowers with beady eyes, Spring Beauties as they are called now. The small voice kept crying: "Awake! the spring is coming!"

Nana-bo-jou said: "Little voice, where are you? Come here."

But the little voice, being everywhere, was nowhere, and could not come at the hero's call.

So he said: "Little voice, you are nowhere because you have no place to live in; I will make you a home."

So Nana-bo-jou took a curl of birch bark and made a little wigwam, and because the voice came from the skies he painted the wigwam with blue mud, and to show that it came from the Sunland he painted a red sun on it. On the floor he spread a scrap of his own white blanket, then for a fire he breathed into it a spark of life, and said: "Here, little voice, is your wigwam." The little voice entered and took possession, but Nana-bo-jou had breathed the spark of life into it. The smoke-vent wings began to move and to flap, and the little wigwam turned into a beautiful Bluebird with a red sun on its breast and a shirt of white. Away it flew, but every year it comes as winter wanes, the Bluebird of the spring. The voice still dwells in it, and we feel that it has lost nothing of its earliest power when we hear it cry: "Awake! the spring is coming!"

TALE 6

Robin, the Bird that Loves to Make Clay Pots

EVERYONE knows the Robin; his reddish-brown breast, gray back, white throat, and dark wings and tail are easily remembered. If you colour the drawing, you will always remember it afterward. The Robin comes about our houses and lawns; it lets us get close enough to see it. It has a loud, sweet song. All birds have a song*; and all sing when they are happy. As they sing most of the time, except when they are asleep, or when moulting, they must have a lot of happiness in their lives.

Here are some things to remember about the Robin. It is one of the earliest of all our birds to get up in the morning, and it begins to sing long before there is daylight.

Birds that live in the trees, *hop;* birds that live on the ground, *walk* or *run;* but the Robin lives partly in the trees and partly on the ground, so sometimes he hops and sometimes he runs.

When he alights on a fence or tree, he looks at you and flashes the white spots on the outer corners of his tail. Again and again he does this. Why? That is his way of letting you know that he is a Robin. He is saying in signal code—flash and wig-wag—"I'm a Robin, I'm a Robin, I'm a Robin." So you will not mistake him for some bird that is less loved.

The Robin invented pottery before men did; his nest is always a clay pot set in a little pile of straws. Sometime,

*Some, like the Turkey-buzzards, have not yet been heard to sing, but I believe they do.

The Robin Making Clay Pots

get a Robin's nest after the bird is done with it; dry it well, put it on the fire very gently; leave it till all the straws are burned away, and then if it does not go to pieces, you will find you have a pretty good earthen pot.

The Robin loves to make these pots. I have known a cock Robin make several which he did not need, just for the fun of making them.

A friend of mine said to me once, "Come, and I will show you the nest of a crazy Robin." We went to the woodshed and there on a beam were six perfectly good Robin nests all in a row; all of them empty.

"There," said my friend. "All of these six were built by a cock Robin in about ten days or two weeks. He seemed to do nothing but sing and build nests. Then after finishing the last one, he disappeared. Wasn't he crazy?"

"No," I said, "not at all. He was not crazy; he was industrious. Let me finish the chapter. The hen Robin was sitting on the eggs, the cock bird had nothing else to do, so he put in the time at the two things he did the best and loved the most: singing and nest-building. Then after the young were hatched in the home nest, he had plenty to do caring for them, so he ceased both building and singing, for that season."

I have often heard of such things. Indeed, they are rather common, but not often noticed, because the Robin does not often build all the extra nests in one place.

Do you know the lovely shade called Robin's-egg blue? The next time you see a Robin's nest with eggs in it you will understand why it was so named and feel for a moment, when first you see it, that you have found a casket full of most exquisite jewels.

Next to nest-building, singing is the Robin's gift, and the songs that he sings are full of joy. He says, "*cheerup, cheerup, cheerily cheer-up*"; and he means it too.

TALE 7

Brook Brownie, or How the Song Sparrow Got His Streaks

His Mother was the Brook and his sisters were the Reeds,
They, every one, applauded when he sang about his deeds.
His vest was white, his mantle brown, as clear as they could be,
And his songs were fairly bubbling o'er with melody and glee.
But an envious Neighbour splashed with mud our Brownie's coat and vest,
And then a final handful threw that stuck upon his breast.
The Brook-bird's mother did her best to wash the stains away;
But there they stuck, and, as it seems, are very like to stay.
And so he wears the splashes and the mud blotch, as you see;
But his songs are bubbling over still with melody and glee.

TALE 8

Diablo and the Dogwood

What a glorious thing is the Maytime Dogwood in our woods! How it does sing out its song! More loudly and clearly it sings than any other spring flower! For it is not one, but a great chorus; and I know it is singing that "The spring, the very spring is in the land!"

I suppose if one had King Solomon's fayland ears, one might hear the Dogwood music like a lot of church bells pealing, like the chorus of the cathedral where Woodthrush is the preacher-priest and the Veeries make responses.

It was Adam's favourite tree, they say, in the Garden of

Brook Brownie

The Dogwood Bloom

Eden. And it grew so high, flowered so wonderfully, and gave so much pleasure that Diablo, who is also called the Devil, wanted to kill it. He made up his mind that he would blight and scatter every shining leaf of its snowy bloom. So one dark night he climbed a Honey Locust tree near the gate, and swung by his tail over the wall, intending to tear off all the lovely blossoms. But he got a shock when he found that every flower was in the *shape of a cross*, which put them beyond his power to blight. He was furious at not being able to destroy its beauty, so did the worst he could. Keeping away from the cross he bit a piece out of the edge of every snowy flower leaf, and then jumped back to the Honey Locust tree.

The Locust was ashamed when she found that she had helped Diablo to do such a mean bit of mischief, so she grew a bristling necklace of strong spikes to wear; they were so long and sharp that no one since, not even Diablo himself, has ever been able to climb that Honey Locust tree.

But it was too late to save the Dogwood bloom. The bites were out, and they never healed up again, as you can see to this very day.

TALE 9

The Woolly-bear

Do you know the Woolly-bear Caterpillar? It is divided into three parts; the middle one brown, the two ends black. Everyone notices the Woolly-bear, because it comes out in early spring, as soon as the frost is over, and crawls on the fences and sidewalks as though they belonged to it. It does not seem to be afraid of any one or anything. It will march across the road in front of a motor car, or crawl up the leg of your boot. Sometimes when you brush it off with your

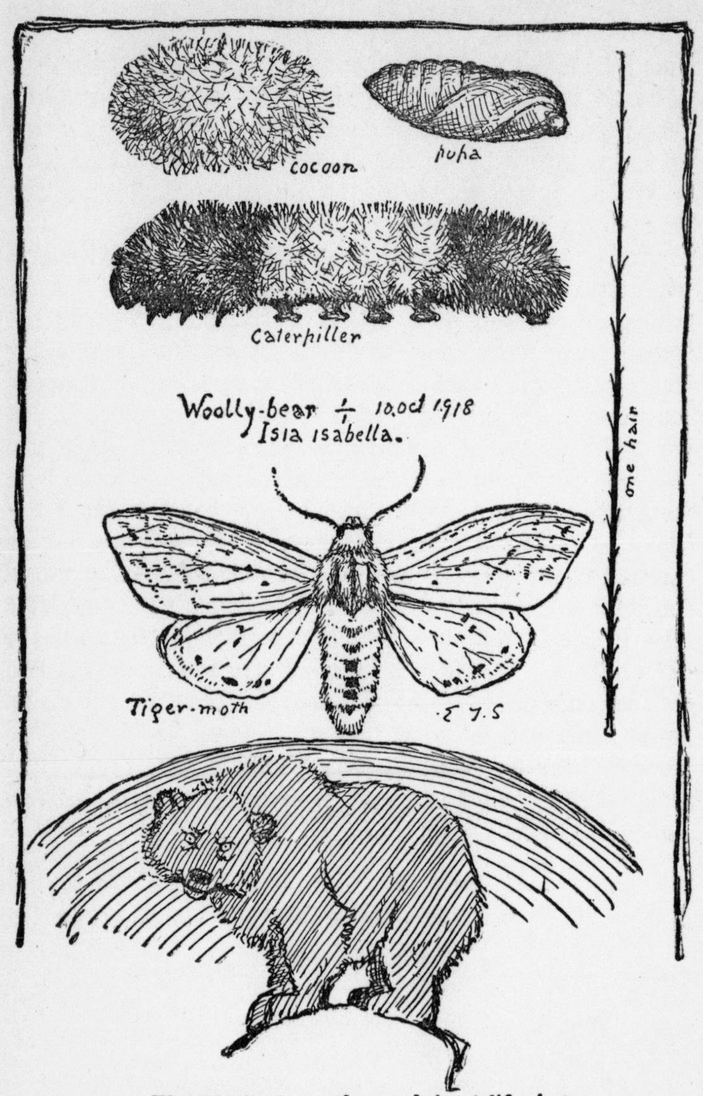

The Woolly-bear (the moth is 1¼ life size)

hand, little hairs are left sticking in your fingers, because it is really like a small porcupine, protected by short spears sticking out of its skin in all directions. Here at the side of the picture, is one of these hairs seen under a microscope.

Where did the Woolly-bear come from? It was hatched from an egg last summer.

And now what is going to happen? It will stuff itself with rib-grass or other low plants, till it has grown bigger; then it will get a warning from the All-mother to prepare for the great change. In some low dry place under a log, stone or fence-rail, it will spin a cocoon with its own spikey hairs outside for a protector. In this rough hairy coffin it will roll itself up, for its "little death," as the Indians call it, and Mother Carey will come along with her sleeping wand, and touch it, so it will go into sound sleep, but for only a few days. One bright sunny morning old Mother Carey comes around again, touches the Woolly-bear bundle-baby, and out of it comes the Woolly-bear, only now it is changed like the Prince in the story into a beautiful Moth called the Tiger-Moth! Out he comes, and if you look up at one end of the coffin he is leaving, you may see the graveclothes he wore when first he went to sleep. Away he flies now to seek his beautiful mate, and soon she lays a lot of eggs, from each of which will come another little Woolly-bear to grow into a big Woolly-bear, and do it all over again.

TALE 10

How the Violets Came

THE Meadow she was sorry
For her sister Sky, you see,
'Cause, though her robe of blue was bright,
'Twas plain as it could be.

And so she sent a skylark up
To trim the Sky robe right
With daisies from the Meadow
(You can see them best at night).

And every scrap of blue cut out
To make those daisies set
Came tumbling down upon the grass
And grew a violet.

TALE 11

Cocoons

EVERYONE loves to go a-hunting. Our forebears were hunters for so many ages that the hunting spirit is strong in all of us, even though held in check by the horror of giving pain to a fellow being. But the pleasure of being outdoors, of seeking for hidden treasures, of finding something that looks at first like old rubbish, and then turns out to be a precious and beautiful thing, that is ours by right of the old law—finders, keepers. That is a kind of hunting that every healthy being loves, and there are many ways and chances for you to enjoy it.

Go out any time between October and April, and look in all the low trees and high bushes for the little natural rag-bundles called "cocoons." Some are bundle-shaped and fast to a twig their whole length. Some hang like a Santa Claus bag on a Christmas tree; but all may be known by their hairiness or the strong, close cover of fine gray or brown fibre or silk, without seams and woven to keep out the wet.

They are so strongly fastened on, that you will have to break the twig to get the bundle down. If it seems very

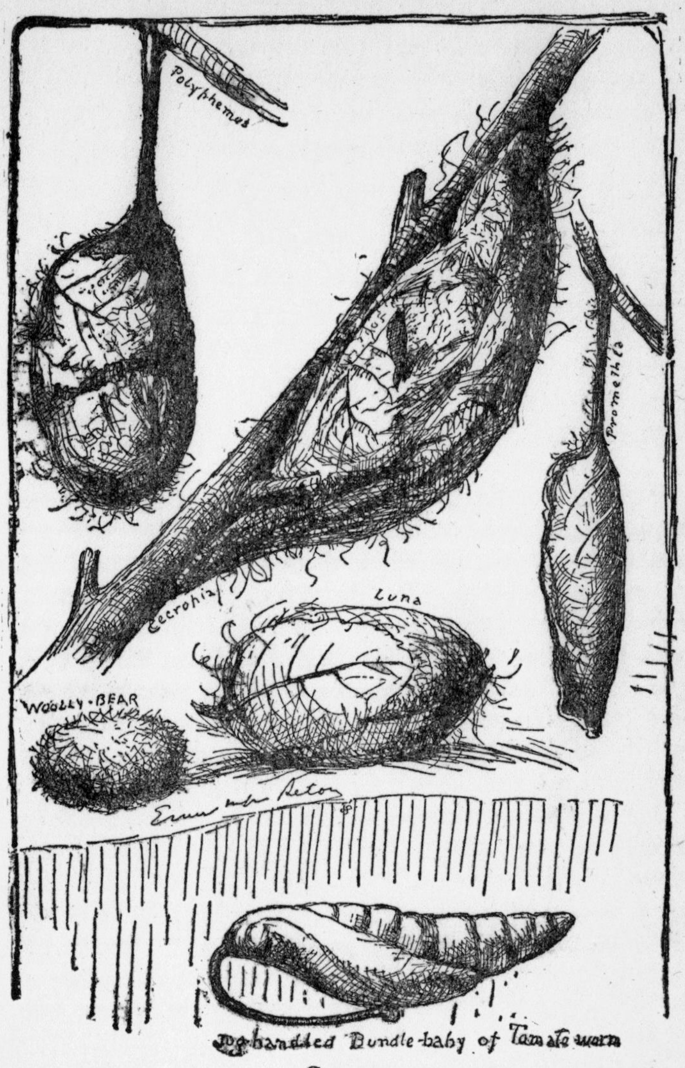
Polyphemus
Cecropia
Luna
Promethea
WOOLLY-BEAR
Jug-handled Bundle-baby of Tomato-worm

Cocoons

light, and rattled when you shake it, you will likely see one or more small, sharp, round holes in it. This means that an insect enemy has destroyed the little creature sleeping within. If the Cocoon is perfect and seems solid and heavy, take it home, and put it in a cardboard, or wooden box, which has a wire screen, or gauze cover. Keep it in a light place, not too dry, till the springtime comes; then one day a miracle will take place. The case will be cut open from within, and out will come a gorgeous Moth. It is like the dull, dark grave opening up at the resurrection to let forth a new-born, different being with wings to fly in the heavens above.

In the drawing I have shown five different kinds of bundlebaby, then at the bottom have added the jug-handled bundle-baby of the Tomato worm; it does not make a Cocoon but buries itself in the ground when the time comes for the Great Sleep. Kind Mother Earth protects it as she does the Hickory Horn-Devil, so it does not need to make a Cocoon at all.

There is a wonderful story about each of these bundle-babies. You will never get weary if you follow and learn them, for each one differs from the last. Some of them I hope to tell you in this book, and before we begin I want you to know some of the things that men of science have learned, and why a Butterfly is not a Moth.

TALE 12

Butterflies and Moths

Do you remember the dear old fairy tale of Beauty and the Beast? How Beauty had to marry the Beast to save her father's life? But as soon as she had bravely agreed to sacrifice herself—as soon as she gave the fateful "Yes" the Beast stood up on his hind legs, his horns, hoofs and hide rolled off, and he was turned back into his true shape, a splendid young Prince whom she could not help loving; and they lived happy ever after.

Do you know that just such transformations and happy weddings are going on about us all the time? The Beast is an ugly Caterpillar, the Princess Beauty is the Butterfly or the Moth. And when the Beast is changed into the Prince Charming and meets with Princess Beauty, they are just as madly happy as they tell it in the fairy books. I know it, for I have seen the transformation, and I have seen the pair go off on their wedding flight.

Men of science have been trying to explain these strange transformations, and to discover why the Prince and Princess do not need to eat or drink, once they have won their highest form, their life of wings and joy. But they have not got much farther than giving names to the things we have long loved and seen as children, dividing the winged wonders into two big families called Butterflies and Moths.

Do you know the difference between a Butterfly and a Moth?

Taken together they make a large group that are called Scale-wings, because they alone among insects, have scales or tiny feathers like dust on the wings. Butterflies are Scale-wings that fly by day, and have club-shaped feelers; they mostly fold one wing against the other when they alight, and in the chrysalis, or bundle-baby stage, they are naked and look like an African ear-drop.

Moths are Scale-wings that fly by night, and have switch or feather-shaped feelers; they keep their wings spread open when they alight, and in the bundle-baby stage, they are wrapped in a cocoon. There are some that do not keep to these rules, but they are rare, and the shape of the feelers will tell whether it is a Moth or a Butterfly.

All of these Scale-wings are hatched from eggs, and come first, as a worm, grub, or caterpillar; next as a chrysalis pupa or bundle-baby; last as the winged creature. That is, first a Beast and last a Beauty. Each of them must at one time be the ugly one, before the great change comes. But I must tell you a truth that the Fairy Books left out, and which maybe you have guessed—Princess Beauty too was at one time forced to live and look like a Beast, till she had fought her own fight, had worked out her own high destiny, and won her way to wings.

TALE 13

The Mourning-cloak Butterfly, or the Camberwell Beauty

There was once a lady who dwelt in Camberwell. She was so good to see that people called her "The Camberwell Beauty." She dressed so magnificently that her robe was covered with gold, and spangled with precious stones of most amazing colours. Especially proud was she, of the row of big blue diamonds that formed the border; and she loved to go forth into the world to see and be seen; although she knew that the country was full of robbers who would be sure to steal her jewels if they could. Then she made a clever plan, she kept on the beautiful things that she loved to dress in, but over all she hung a black velvet mourning cloak which nobody could possibly want to steal. Then she went up and down the roads as much as she pleased.

Well, this story may be not quite true, but it is partly true, and the beautiful lady is known to-day as the Mourning-cloak Butterfly. There it is, plain to be seen, the black mourning cloak, but peeping from under it, you can see the

Mourning-cloak Butterfly (¾ life size)

golden border and some of the blue diamonds too, if you look very carefully.

In the North Woods where I spent my young days, the first butterfly to be seen in the springtime was the Mourning-cloak, and the reason we saw it so early in the season, yes, even in the snowtime, was because this is one of the Butterflies that sometimes sleep all winter, and so live in two different seasons.

Its eggs are laid on the willows, elms, or poplars, in early springtime. The young soon hatch, and eat so much, and grow so fast, that five weeks after the eggs are laid, and three after they are hatched, the caterpillar is full grown, and hangs itself up as a chrysalis under some sheltering board or rail. In two weeks more, the wonderful event takes place, the perfect Butterfly comes forth; and there is another Mourning-cloak to liven the roadside, and amaze us with its half-hidden beauty.

TALE 14

The Wandering Monarch

Did you ever read the old Greek story of Ulysses, King of Ithaca, the Wandering Monarch, who for twenty years roamed over sea and land away from home—always trying to get back, but doomed to keep on travelling, homesick and weary, but still moving on; until his name became a byword for wandering?

In our own woods and our own fields in America we have a Wandering Monarch—the "Big Red Butterfly" as we children called it—the "Monarch" as it is named by the butterfly catchers.

It is called the "Wanderer" chiefly because it is the only one of our Butterflies that migrates like the birds. In the

MONARCH BUTTERFLY
"The Wanderer" in Three Stages: Cocoon, Caterpillar, and Butterfly

late summer it gathers in great swarms when the bright days are waning, and flies away to warmer lands. I have often seen it going, yet I do not remember that I ever saw it come back in the springtime; but it comes, though not in great flocks like those that went south.

One of the common names of this splendid creature is "Milkweed Butterfly" because its grub or caterpillar is fond of feeding on the leaves of the common milkweed.

The drawing shows the size and style of the grub; in colour it is yellow or yellowish green with black bands.

As soon as it is grown big enough and fat enough, the grub hangs itself up as a "chrysalis" which is a Greek word that may be freely rendered into "golden jewel." The middle drawing shows its shape; in colour it is of a pale green with spots of gold, or as it has been described "a green house with golden nails."

After about two weeks the great change takes place, and the bundle-baby or chrysalis opens to let out the splendid red-brown Butterfly, of nearly the same red as a Cock Robin's breast in springtime, with lines and embroidery of black and its border set with pearls. Near the middle of the hind wing is a dark spot like a thickening of one rib. This has been called a "sachet bag" or "scent-pocket," and though not very ornamental to look at, is of more use to it than the most beautiful white pearl of the border. For this is the battery of its wireless telegraph. We think our ships and aeroplanes very far advanced because they can signal miles away, and yet the Wandering Monarch had an outfit for sending messages long before it was ever dreamed of by man. Maybe it is not a very strong battery, but it certainly reaches for miles; and maybe its messages are not very clear, but they serve at least to let the Monarchs know where their wives are, and how to find them, which is something.

There is one other reason for calling this the Wanderer. Although it is an American by birth, it has travelled to England and the Philippines and is ever going farther over the world till at last no doubt it will have seen all lands and possessed them.

It makes old Ulysses look like a very stay-at-home, for his farthest travels never went beyond the blue Mediterranean, and his whole twenty years of voyaging covered less than the states east of the Mississippi—much less than our Red Wanderer covers in a single summer.

TALE 15

The Bells of the Solomon Seal

LET us go out into the woods, and look for the Solomon Seal. This is May and we should find it in some half open place, where it is neither wet nor dry. Here it is! See the string of bells that hangs from its curving stem. Dig out its roots, wash off the earth, and you will see the mark of King Solomon's Seal that gives its name to the plant. Now listen to the story of it all.

King Solomon had the "second sight" that means the deeper sight, the magic eyesight which made him see through a stone wall, or read men's thoughts. King Solomon had fayland ears; which means, he could hear all sounds from A to Z; while common ears, like yours and mine, hear only the middle sounds from K to Q.

Everything that lives and moves is giving out music; every flower that blooms is singing its song. We cannot hear, our ears are too dull; but King Solomon could. And one day, as he walked through the woods, he heard a new flower-song that made him stop and listen. It had strange music with it, and part of that was a chime of golden bells.

The Bells of the Solomon Seal

The great King sat down on a bank. His fayland eyes could see right into the ground. He saw the fat fleshy root like a little goblin, reaching its long white fingers down into the soil, picking out the magic crystals to pack away in its pockets; and he could see the tall stem like a wood-elf carrying them up, and spreading them upon its flat hands, so they could soak up the juices of the sun and air. He could see them turning into a wonderful stuff like amber dew, with a tang like new-cut timber. But it was not yet done, so he could not tell just what it might be good for. Now it was springtime, and it would be harvest red moon before the little worker would have the magic healing stored in its treasure bags underground. So to prevent any one harming or hindering the plant till its work was done, the King took out his seal ring and stamped seal marks all along the root, where they are unto this day. And then to make it sure he made the golden bell chimes become visible so every one could see them. There they hang like a row of ringing bells.

But the King never came back to learn the rest of it, for he had to build the temple; and he had many wives who took up a great deal of his time. So the world has never found out just what is the magic power of the plant. But it is there, be sure of that, just as surely as the peal of golden bells is there, and the marks of the great King's Seal.

TALE 16

The Silver Bells of the False Solomon Seal

Over a month later, the King suddenly remembered that he had not been out to see the plant whose root he had sealed. He was very busy at the time, as he had the temple to build, and many wives to look after; so he called Djin, a good

The Silver Bells of the False Solomon Seal

goblin, who does hard work and said, "Go and see that no one has harmed that plant," then told him how to find it.

Away went the good goblin, like a flash. He was a very obedient servant, but not very bright; and when he came to the woods, he looked all around for the plant with the chime of bells, for King Solomon had forgotten to say that the bells do not ring after June, and it was now July. So the goblin looked about for a long time. He did not dare to go back and say he could not find it—that would have been a terrible crime, so he looked and looked. At last he heard a little tinkle of bells away off in the woods. He flew to the place, and there was a plant like the one he sought but its bells were of silver, and all in a bunch instead of a long string. The good goblin dug down to the big fat root in the ground and found that the seal marks had grown over—at least he thought they had—for they were nowhere to be seen. So he looked around for something to help. His eye fell on an acorn cup. He took this, and using it for a seal, he stamped the root all over.

Then he took a piece of the root and a sprig and flew back to show the King. Solomon smiled and said: "You did the best you could, but you have marked the wrong root. Listen! This is not the golden chime, but the chime of silver bells."

That is the story of it and that is why it has ever since been called the False Solomon Seal.

THINGS TO SEE IN SUMMERTIME

The Brownie and the
Mouse-bird

Things to See in Summertime

TALE 17

How the Mouse-bird Made Fun of the Brownie

ONCE there was a conceited Brownie, who thought he could do more things and do them better than any other of his people. He had not tried yet, for he was very young, but he said he was going to do them some day!

One morning a sly old Brownie, really making fun of him, said: "Why don't you catch that Phoebe-bird? It is quite easy if you put a little salt on his tail." Away went Smarty Brownie to try. But the Phoebe would not sit still, and the Brownie came back saying: "He bobbed his tail so, the salt would not stay on."

"Well," said the sly old Brownie, "there is a little Mouse-bird whose tail never bobs. You can easily catch him, for you see, he does not even fly, but crawls like a mouse up the tree," and he pointed to a little brown Creeper. By this time the young Brownie knew that the others were laughing at him, so he said rather hotly, "I'll just show you right now."

He took an acorn cup full of salt, and went after the Mouse-bird. It was at the bottom of the big tree, creeping up, round and round, as if on a spiral staircase, and the Brownie began to climb in the same way. But every little while the climber had to stop and rest. This had strange results, for there is a law in Brownie land, that wherever one of the little people stops to sit down, or rest, a toadstool must spring up for him to sit on. So the track of the Brownie up the trunk became one long staircase of toadstool steps, some close, some far apart, but each showing where the Brownie had rested. They came closer together toward the top where the Brownie had got tired, but he was coming very near to the Creeper now. He got his pinch of salt all ready, as his friends down below kept calling and jeering: "Now you've got him, now is your chance." But just as he was going to leap forward and drop the salt on its tail, the Creeper gave a tiny little laugh like "*Tee-tee-tee*," spread its wings, for it could fly very well, and sailed away to the bottom of the next tree to do the spiral staircase all over again, while Smarty Brownie was so mad that he jumped to the ground and hid away from his friends for two days. When he came back he did not talk quite so much as he used to. But to this day you can see the staircase of toadstools on the tree trunks where the Brownie went up.

TALE 18

The Pot-herb that Sailed with the Pilgrims

"COME," said the Guide, "to-day I am going to show you a Pot-herb that came from England with the Pilgrim Fathers and spread over the whole of America. There is a story about it that will keep it ever in your memory."

The Pilgrims had landed in Massachusetts, and slowly made farms for themselves as they cleared off the forest. They had a very hard time at first, but the Indians helped them; sometimes with gifts of venison, and sometimes by showing them which things in the woods were good to eat.

There was a Squaw named Monapini, "the Root-digger,"

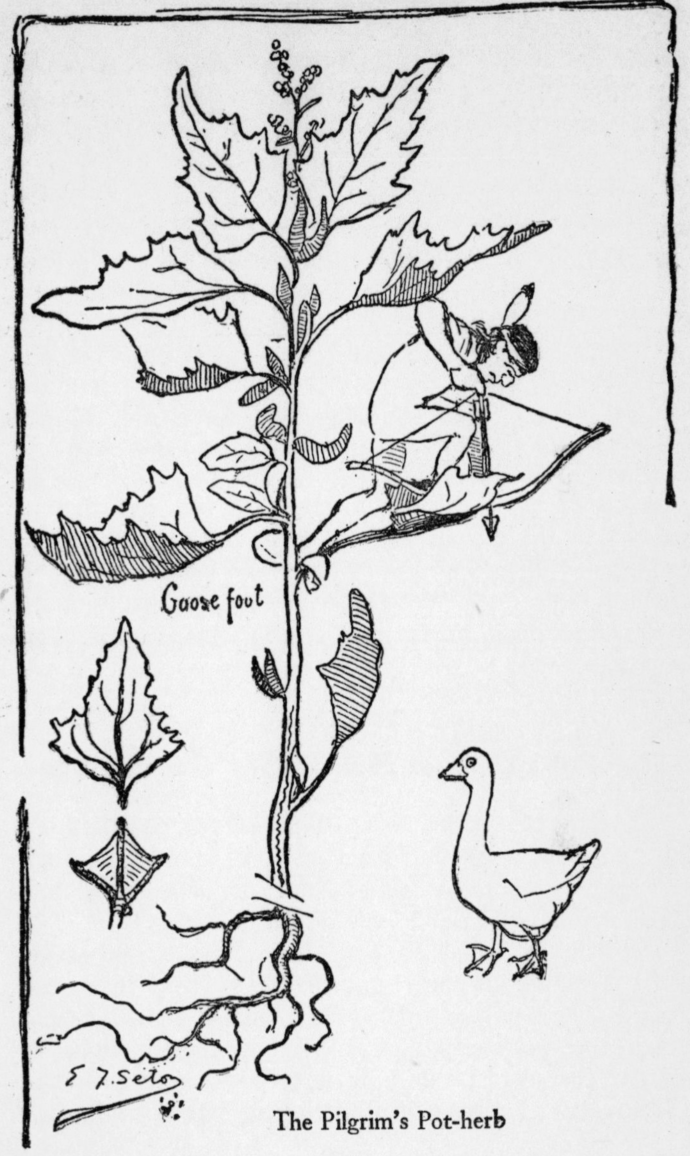

The Pilgrim's Pot-herb

who was very clever at finding forest foods. She became friendly with a white woman named Ruth Pilgrim, and so Ruth's family got the benefit of it, and always had on the table many good things that came from the woods.

One day, long after the farms were cleared and doing well, the white woman said, "See, Mother Monapini, thou hast shown me many things, now I have somewhat to show thee. There hath grown up in our wheat field a small herb that must have come from England with the wheat, for hitherto I have not seen it elsewhere. We call it lamb's-quarter, for the lamb doth eat it by choice. Or maybe because we do eat it with a quarter of lamb. Nevertheless it maketh a good pot-herb when boiled."

The old Indian woman's eyes were fixed on the new plant that was good to eat: and she said, "Is it very good, oh white sister?"

"Yes, and our medicine men do say that it driveth out the poison that maketh itch and spots on the skin." After a moment Monapini said, "It looketh to me like the foot of a wild goose."

"Well found," chuckled Ruth, "for sometimes our people do call it by that very name."

"That tells me different," said the Indian.

"What mean you," said Ruth.

"Is not a goose foot very strong, so it never catcheth cold in the icy water?"

"Yes."

"And this hath the shape of a goose foot?"

"Yes."

"Then my Shaman tells that it is by such likeness that the Great Spirit showeth the goose foot plant to be charged with the driving out of colds."

"It may be so," said the white woman, "but this I know. It is very good and helpeth the whole body."

The Indian picked a handful of the pot-herbs, then stared hard at the last; a very tall and strong one.

"What hast thou now, Monapini?" The red woman pointed to the stem of the lamb's-quarter, whereon were long red streaks, and said: "This I see, that, even as the white-man's herb came over the sea and was harmless and clean while it was weak, but grew strong and possessed this field, then was streaked to midheight with blood, so also shall they be who brought it—streaked at last to the very waist with blood—not the white men's but the dark purple blood of the Indian. This the voices tell me is in the coming years, that this is what we shall get again for helping you—destruction in return for kindness. Mine inner eyes have seen it." She threw down the new pot-herb and glided away, to be seen no more in the settlements of the white men.

And Ruth, as she gazed after her, knew that it was true. Had she not heard her people talking and planning? For even as the weed seed came with the wheat, so evil spirits came with the God-fearing Pilgrims, and already these were planning to put the heathens to the sword, when the Colony was strong enough.

So the Indian woman read the truth in the little pot-herb that sailed and landed with the Pilgrims; that stands in our fields to this day, streaked with the blood of the passing race—standing, a thing of remembrance.

TALE 19

How the Red Clover Got the White Mark on Its Leaves

ONCE upon a time a Bee, a Bug, and a Cow went marching up to Mother Carey's palace in the hemlock grove, to tell her of their troubles. They complained that food was poor

How the Red Clover Got the White Mark on Its Leaves

and scarce, and they were tired of the kinds that grew along the roadsides.

Mother Carey heard them patiently, then she said: "Yes, you have some reason to complain, so I will send you a new food called Clover. Its flower shall be full of honey for the Bee, its leaves full of cowfood and its cellar shall be stocked with tiny pudding bags of meal for the Bug, that is for good little Bug-folks who live underground."

Now the tribes of the Bee, the Bug, and the Cow had a fine time feasting, for the new food was everywhere.

But Cows are rather stupid you know. They found the new food so good that they kept on munching everything that had three round leaves, thinking it was Clover, and very soon a lot of them were poisoned with strange plants that no wise Cow would think of eating.

So Mother Carey called a Busy Brownie, and put him on guard to keep the Cows from eating the poison plants by mistake.

At first it was good fun, and the Brownie enjoyed it because it made him feel important. But he got very tired of his job and wanted to go to the ball game.

He sat down on a toadstool, and looked very glum. He could hear the other Brownies shouting at the game, and that made him feel worse. Then he heard a great uproar, and voices yelling "A home run!" "A home run!" That drove him wild. He had been whittling the edge of the toadstool with his knife, and now he slashed off a big piece of the cap, he was so mad.

Then up he got and said to the Cows: "See here, you fool Cows, I can't stay here for ever trying to keep you from eating poison, but I'll do this much. I'll stamp all the good-to-eat leaves with a mark that will be your guide."

So he made a rubber stamp out of part of the toadstool

The Shamrock

he was sitting on, and stamped every Clover leaf in that pasture, so the Cows could be sure, then skipped away to the ball game.

When Mother Carey heard of his running away from his job, she was very angry. She said: "Well, you Bad Brownie, you should be ashamed, but that white mark was a good idea so I'll forgive you, if you go round, and put it on every Clover leaf in the world."

He had to do it, though it looked like an endless task, and he never would have finished it, had not the other Brownies all over the world come to help him; so it was done at last. And that is the reason that every Clover leaf to-day has on it the white mark like an arrowhead, the Brownie sign for "good-to eat."

The Cows get along better now, but still they are very stupid; they go munching ahead without thinking, and will even eat the blossoms which belong to the Bees. And the Bees have to buzz very loudly and even sting the Cows on their noses to keep them from stealing the bee-food. The good little Bugs underground have the best time, for there the Cows can not harm them, and the Bees never come near. They eat when they are hungry and sleep when they are cold, which is their idea of a good time; so except for some little quarrels between the Cows and the Bees they have all gotten along very well ever since.

TALE 20

The Shamrock and Her Three Sisters

The Shamrock is really the White Clover. It is much the same shape as the Red Clover, and has the same food bags in its cellar. It is just as good for Cows and even better for Bees; so the Brownie stamped all its leaves with

Yellow-haired Hop,
Shamrock's
blonde
sister

the white arrow mark, as you can plainly see. This plant, as you know, is the emblem of Ireland.

The story-tellers say that St. Patrick was preaching to Leary, the heathen King of Tara in Ireland hoping to turn him into a Christian. The king listened attentively, but he was puzzled by St. Patrick's account of the Trinity. "Stop," said the king. "How can there be three Gods in one and only one God where there are three. That is impossible." St. Patrick stooped down and picking up a Shamrock leaf, said: "See, there it is, growing in your own soil; there are three parts but only one leaf." The king was so much struck by this proof that he became a Christian and ever since the Shamrock has been the emblem of Ireland.

Now to fill out the history of the Clovers, I should tell you of the other three. The next is called Alsike, or the Pink Clover.

When you look at this Alsike or Alsatian Clover, you might think its mother was a red clover and its father a white one, for it is about half way between them in size, and its bloom is pink on the outside and white in the middle. Evidently, the Brownie didn't think much of it, for he did not put his arrow mark on its leaves. Still the Cows think it is good, the Bees think it is fine, and it always carried lots of food bags in its cellar. So also does the next sister—Melilot, the Yellow Clover or Honey-lotus— and the last and sweetest of them all, is the Sweet Clover that spreads sweet smells in the old-fashioned garden.

TALE 21

The Indian Basket-maker

"Come, little Nagami, my Bird-Singer, you are ten years old, it is time you learned to make baskets. I made

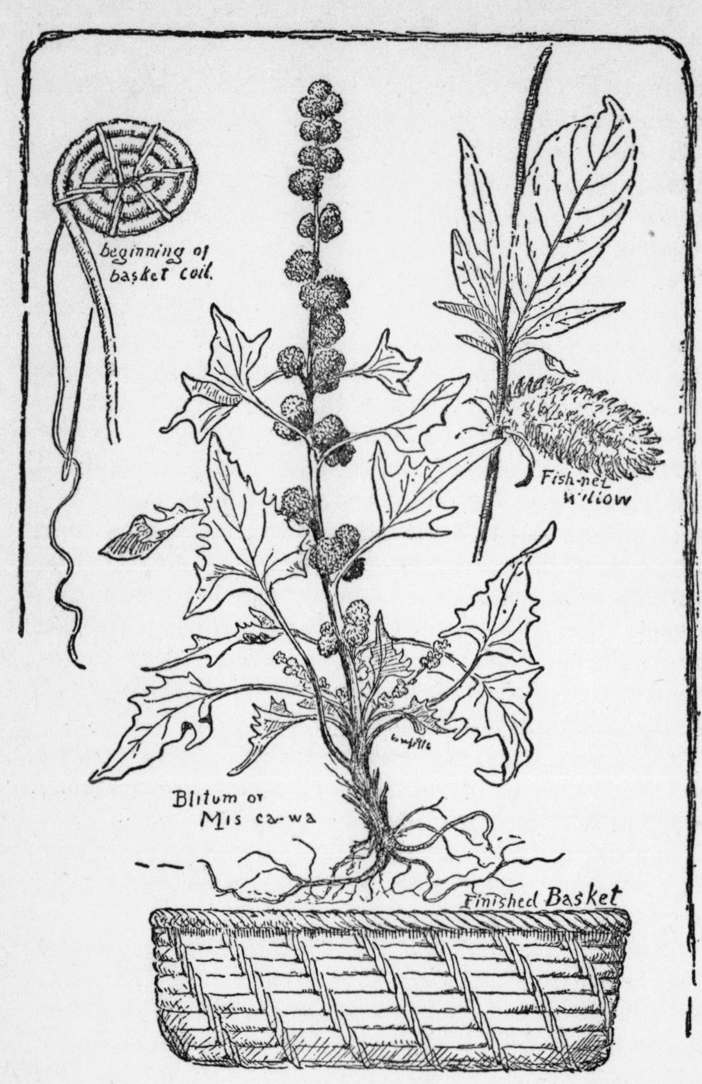

The Indian Basket

my first when I was but eight," said Mother Akoko proudly, for she was the best basket-maker on the river.

So they took a sharp stick, and went into the woods. Akoko looked for spruce trees that had been blown down by the storm, but found none, so she stopped under some standing spruce, at a place with no underbrush and said: "See, Nagami, here we dig for wattap."

The spruce roots or "wattap" were near the surface and easily found, but not easily got out, because they were long, tangled and criss-crossed. Yet, by pulling up, and cutting under, they soon got a bundle of roots like cords, and of different lengths, from two feet to a yard, or more.

"Good," said Akoko; "this is enough and we need not soak them, for it is summer, and the sap is running. If it were fall we should have to boil them. Now you must scrape them clear of the brown bark." So Nagami took her knife and worked for an hour, then came with the bundle saying: "See, Mother, they are smooth, and so white that they have not a brown spot left." "Good," said Akoko, "now you need some bark of the willow for sewing cord. Let us look along the river bank."

There they found the round-leafed, or fish-net willow, and stripped off enough of its strong bark to make a bundle as big as one hand could hold.

This also had to be scraped clear of the brown skin, leaving only the strong whitish inner bark, which, when split into strips, was good for sewing.

"See, my Nagami, when I was a little girl I had only a bone needle made from the leg of a deer, but you have easy work; here is a big steel packing needle, which I bought for you from a trader. This is how you make your basket."

So Akoko began a flat coil with the spruce roots, and sewed it together with the willow bark for thread, until it was a span wide. And whenever a new root was to be added, she cut both old piece and new, to a long point, so they would overlap without a bump.

Then the next coil of the spruce roots was laid on, not flat and level, but raised a little. Also the next, until the walls were as high as four fingers. Then Akoko said, "Good, that is enough. It is a fine corn basket. But we must give it a red rim for good luck."

So they sought in a sunny place along the shore, and found the fruit of the squawberry or blitum. "See," said Akoko, "the miscawa. Gather a handful, my Nagami. They make the red basket-dye."

They crushed the rich red berries, saving the red juice in a clam shell, and soaked a few strands of the white willow bark in the stain. When they were dry, Nagami was taught to add a rim to her basket, by sewing it over and over as in the picture.

Then Akoko said, "Good, my little Bird-Singer, you have done well, you have made some old black roots into a beautiful basket."

N.B. The Guide will remember that rattan and raffia can be used for this when it is impossible to get spruce roots and willow bark. Good dyes may be made from many different berries.

TALE 22

Crinkleroot; or Who Hid the Salad?

It has long been the custom of the Brownies to have a great feast on the first of the merry month of May, to celebrate the return of the spring.

One springtime long ago, they got ready as usual. The King of the Brownies had invited all the leaders; the place for the dinner was chosen in a grove of mandrakes

The Crinkleroot; or Who Hid the Salad?

whose flat umbrellas made a perfect roof, rain or shine. The Bell Bird, whose other name is Wood Thrush, was ringing his bell, and calling all the Chief Brownies by name.

"Ta-rool-ya! *ting-a-ling-ling-ling.*"

"Oka-lee! *ting-a-ling-ling-ling.*"

"Cherk! *ting-a-ling-ling-ling.*"

"Come to the feasting! *ting-a-ling-ling-ling.*"

A hundred glow worms were told to hurry up with their lights and be ready for that night, and busy Brownies gathered good things from woods and waters, for the feast.

May Day came bright and beautiful. The busy ones had all the "eats" in the Mandrake Hall, the glowworms were sleeping soundly to fill their storage batteries ready for the night. It made the salamanders' mouths water to see so many good things; but they were not asked, so stayed away. There were dewdrops in acorn cups, and honey on the wax. There were clam shells piled up with red checkerberries, and caddis worms on the half shell, with spicebush nubbins. A huge white Mecha-meck was the chief dish, with bog nuts on the side. There were lovely long crinkle salads. And last, there were gumdrops from the sweet birch, while at each place was a pussy willow to dust the food over with golden pollen that gave it a pleasant peppery tang. All the guests were there, and the feast was nearly over, when a terrible thing took place!

Of all the dreaded happenings in the world of beauty there is nothing else so feared as the forest fire. There is not much danger of it in springtime, but it is possible at any season, after a long dry spell. Words cannot tell of the horror it spreads, as it comes raging through the woods destroying all beautiful living things.

And right in the middle of the feast, the dreadful news was carried by a flying Night-bird.

"Fire, Fire, Fire, Fire!" he screamed, and almost at once the smoke came drifting through the banquet hall, so they knew it was true.

There was mad haste to escape, and only two ways were open. One was to get across some big stream, and the other was to hide in a cave underground. The birds took the first way, and the Brownies the second. Every Woodchuck den was just packed with Brownies within a few minutes. But the busy Brownie who was chief steward and had charge of the feast, had no idea of leaving all the good things to burn up, if he could help it. First he sent six of his helpers to make a deep pit for the big Mechameck, and while they did that he began hiding all the dishes in the ground. Last he dug some deep holes and quickly buried all the crinkle salads; then he ran for his life into a cave.

The raging fire came along. It is too horrible to tell about, for it was sent by the Evil One. The lovely woods were left black without a living thing. But the very next day, Mother Carey and Mother Earth and El Sol, set about saving the wreck, and in a marvellously short time actually had made it green again. The mayflowers came up a second time that year, the violets came back, and in each place where the Brownies had hid a salad there came up a curious plant that never had been seen before. It had three saw-edged leaves and a long wand, much like the one carried by the Chief Steward. I never was able to find out his name for sure, but I think it was Trileaf or Three-leaves. Anyway, if you dig under his sign and sceptre wand, you will surely find the salad, and very good indeed it is to eat; it was not hurt in the least by the fire.

The Mecha-meck

But from that day, the Brownies have been very shy of feasting during dry weather in the woods. They generally have their banquets now in some meadow, and afterward you can tell the place of the feast by the circle of little toadstools called fairy rings. For you know that wherever a Brownie sits, a toadstool must spring up for him to sit on.

TALE 23

The Mecha-meck

THAT fearful time when the forest fire set all the Brownies busy burying their food and dishes at the feast-hall, you remember it took six of them to carry and hide the Mecha-meck. For it is a large fat white root as big as a baby, and sometimes it has arms or legs, so that when Monapini told Ruth Pilgrim about it she called it "Man-of-the-earth."

You remember that the busy Brownie hid all the Crinkle salads, and so saved them; and most of us have found the Crinkleroot and eaten it since. But how many of us have found the Mecha-meck? I know only one man who has. We call him the Wise Woodman. He found and dug out the one from which I made the picture. It was two and a half feet long and weighed fifteen pounds—fifteen pounds of good food. Think of it! Above it and growing out of its hiding place was a long trailing vine that looked like a white morning-glory. There is always one of these over the Mecha-meck. And by that you may find it, if you look along the sunny banks outside of the woods. But still it is very hard to find. I never yet got one, though I have found many of the crinkle-root salads. Of course, that is easy to explain, for the busy Brownies

DUTCHMAN'S DIVE
E. T. Seton
Dutchmans Breeches
5 May. 1920.

buried hundreds of the salads, but only one of the big fat Mecha-meck.

TALE 24

Dutchman's Breeches

Of course they are not, for no Dutchman I ever saw could wear such tiny things. I will tell you what they really are and how that came to be.

You remember how the Brownies assembled for the feast on May Day when the Glow worms were the lamps and the Wood Thrush rang the bell. Well, it so happened that day that a great crowd of the merrymakers gathered long before the feast was ready, and while they were wondering what to do someone shouted: "See, how fine and warm the water is where the brook spreads out into the ditch. Let us have our first swim of the season right now!"

So they all went with a whoop! stripped off their clothes, and into their swimming breeches with a perfect riot of glee.

Then how they did splash! Some blind folks thought it must be a million early pollywogs splashing. But the swim ended with another racket when the dinner bell rang.

Each splashing Brownie hopped out and hung up his breeches to dry as he got into his clothes.

Then you remember the fire came along and scared them away. Of course the breeches were wet, so they didn't get singed; and there you can see them hanging to this day on the first of May. That is what they really are—Brownies' Breeches. And because the Brownies often swim in a ditch, they are called ditch-man's breeches; but believe me, they are not Dutchman's breeches and never could be.

The Seven Sour Sisters

TALE 25

The Seven Sour Sisters

IF YOU look along any half-open bank in the edge of the woods, or even in the woods itself, you are sure to see one of the Seven Sorrel Sisters, with leaves a little like Clover, only notched in the end and without the white marks, that the Brownie put on the Clover. There are seven of them, according to most doctors; five have yellow eyes, one purple, and one white streaked with blood. Their Latin name means "vinegar" and their Greek name means "acid." "Sorrel" itself means "Little sour one," so you see they have the reputation of a sour bunch. If you eat one of the leaves, you will agree that the name was well-chosen, and understand why the druggists get the tart "salt of lemons" from this family. The French use these Sour Sisters for their sour soup. But in spite of their unsweetness, they are among the pretty things of the woods; their forms are delicate and graceful; their eyes are like jewels, and when the night comes down, they bow their heads, gracefully fold their hands, and sleep like a lot of tired children.

TALE 26

Self-heal or Blue-curls in the Grass

YOU should know the history of the lowly little flower called Blue-curls; and you must remember that flowers have their troubles just as you have. For one thing, flowers must get their pollen or yellow flower-dust, carried to some other of their kind, or they cannot keep on growing good seed. And since the flower cannot walk about finding places for its pollen, it generally makes a bargain with a bee. It says, "If you will carry my pollen to my cousins

Self-heal or Blue-curls in the Grass

yonder, I will give you a sweet sip of nectar." That is where the bees get the stuff for all their honey, and that is how the pollen is carried.

Well, the modest little Blue-curls long had had a working agreement with the Meadow Bees, and got on nicely. But one summer Blue-curls became discontented. She saw all the other plants with wonderful gifts that had power to cure pain and sickness; while she was doing nothing but live her own easy life, and she felt she was a nobody.

So one day as Mother Carey's slowest steed was swishing over the grass, Blue-curls cried out: "Mother Carey, Mother Carey, won't you hear me and grant me a gift?"

"What is it, little one?" said the All-mother.

"Oh, Mother Carey, the pansy cures heartache, the monkshood cures canker-lip, the tansy cures colds, and all the others have some joy and honour of service, but I am good for nothing, Mother Carey so the wise men despise me. Won't you give me a job? Won't you give me some little power?"

"Little one, such an asking never finds me deaf. I love those who would help. I will give you a little bit of *all healing* so that you shall be good medicine, if not the best, for all ills, and men shall call you 'Self-heal' and 'All-heal' for you shall have all healing in yourself."

And it has been so ever since. So that some who go by looks call the modest little meadow flower, "Blue-curls in the Grass," but the old herb-men who know her goodness call her "All-heal" or "Self-heal."

TALE 27

The Four Butterflies You See Every Summer

THERE are four Butterflies that you are sure to see every summer, on our fields; and remember that each of them goes through the same changes. First it is an egg, then a greedy

Summer Butterflies (a little over life size)

grub, next a hanging bundle-baby, and last a beautiful winged fairy, living a life of freedom and joy.

In the picture I have shown the butterflies life size, but you must add the colour as you get each one to copy.

The first is the *White* or *Cabbage Butterfly* that flits over our gardens all summer long.

It is not a true American, but came from Europe in 1860 and landed at Quebec, from whence it has spread all over the country. In the drawing I have shown the female; the male is nearly the same but has only one round dark spot on the front wings. Its grub is a little naked green caterpillar, that eats very nearly a million dollars' worth of cabbages a year; so it is a pity it was ever allowed to land in this country. There are moths that we should like to get rid of, but this is the only butterfly that is a pest.

2nd. The *Yellow* or *Clouded Sulphur Butterfly*. You are sure to find it, as soon as you begin to look for butterflies. This is the one that is often seen in flocks about mud puddles.

When I was a very small boy, I once caught a dozen of them, and made a little beehive to hold them, thinking that they would settle down and make themselves at home, just like bees or pigeons. But the grown-ups made me let them fly away, for the Sulphur is a kindly creature, and does little or no harm.

One of the most beautiful things I ever came across, was, when about ten years old, I saw on a fence stake ahead of me a big bird that was red, white and blue, with a flaming yellow fan-crest. Then as I came closer, I knew that it was a red-headed woodpecker, with a Sulphur Butterfly in his beak; this made the crest; what I thought was blue turned out to be his glossy black back reflecting the blue sky.

3rd. The next is the *Red Admiral* or *Nettle Butterfly*. The "red" part of the name is right, but why "Admiral"? I never could see unless it was misprint for "Admirable."

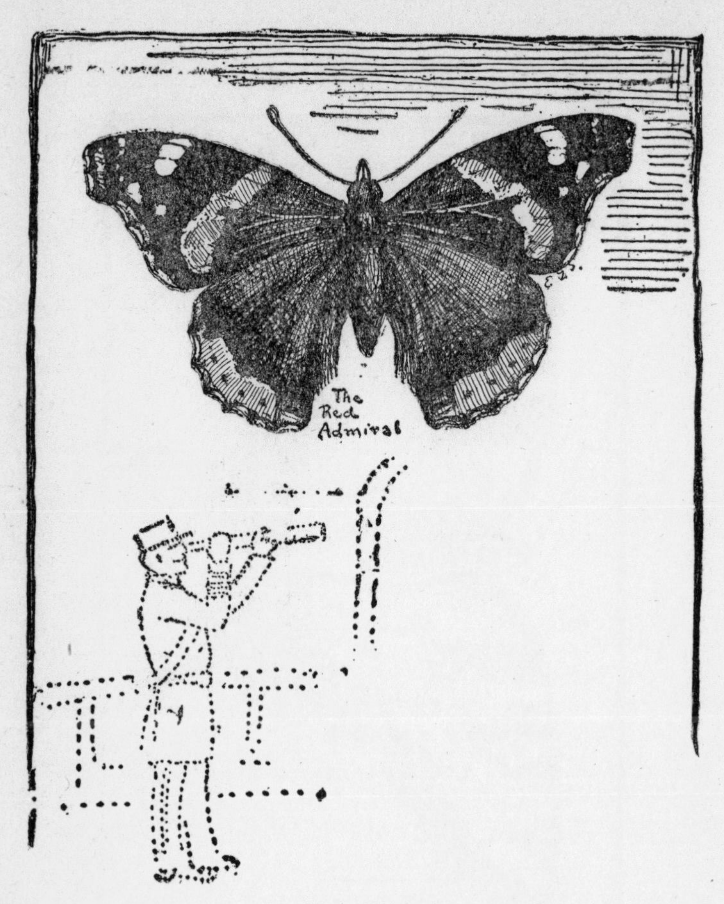

Red Admiral

Tiger Swallowtail (life size)

This beautiful insect lays its eggs and raises its young on nettles, and where nettles are, there is the Red Admiral also. And that means over nearly all the world! Its caterpillar is not very well protected with bristles, not at all when compared with the Woolly-bear, but it lives in the nettles, and, whether they like it or not, the hospitable nettles with their stings protect the caterpillar. The crawler may be grateful, but he shows it in a poor way, for he turns on the faithful nettle, and eats it up. In fact the only food he cares about is nettle-salad, and he indulges in it several times a day, yes all day long, eating, growing and bursting his skin a number of times, till he is big enough to hang himself up for the winter, probably in a nettle. Then next spring he comes forth, in the full dress uniform of a Red Admiral, gold lace, red sash, silver braid and all.

4th. The last of the four is the *Tiger Swallowtail.* You are sure to see it some day—the big yellow butterfly that is striped like a tiger, with peacock's feathers in its train, and two long prongs, like a swallow-tail, to finish off with. It is found in nearly all parts of the Eastern States and Canada. I saw great flocks of them on the Slave River of the North.

It is remarkable in that there are both blondes and brunettes among its ladies. The one shown in the drawing is a blonde. The brunettes are so much darker as to be nearly black; and so different that at one time everyone thought they were of a different kind altogether.

TALE 28

The Beautiful Poison Caterpillar

THE lovely Io Moth is one that you will see early, and never forget, for it is common, and ranges over all the

The Beautiful Poison Caterpillar (the moth is a little over life size)

country from Canada to the Gulf. When you see it, you will be inclined to spell its name Eye-oh—for it has on each wing a splendid eye like that on a peacock's tail-feather, while the rest of its dress is brown velvet and gold.

There is a strange chapter in the life of Io, which you should know because it shows that Mother Carey never gives any wonderful gift to her creatures without also giving with it some equal burden of sorrow.

This is how it all came about.

Long ago when the little ones of the Io Moth were small, they were, like most caterpillars, very ugly little things. They felt very badly about it, and so they set out one day for the great Home Place of Mother Carey in the Whispering Grove of the Ages.

There they prayed, "Dear Mother Carey, we are not of an ugly race, why should we be so ugly as caterpillars? Will you not make us beautiful, for beauty is one of the best things of all?"

Mother Carey smiled and waved a finger toward a little Brownie, who came with a tray on which were two cups; one full of bright sparkling pink stuff, and the other with something that looked like dark green oil. But the glasses were joined at the top, there was but one place to drink, and that reached both.

Then Mother Carey said, "These are the goblets of life, one is balm and will give you joy, the other is gall and will give you suffering. You may drink little or much, but you must drink equally of both. Now what would ye?"

The little ugly creatures whispered together, then one said: "Mother Carey, if we drink, will it give us beauty?"

"Yes, my children, the red goblet of life will give you beauty, but with it the other will give you grief."

They whispered together, then all the little crawlers

went silently forward, and each took a long drink of the double goblet.

Then they crawled away, and at once became the most beautiful of all caterpillars, brilliant jewel-green with stripes of pink, velvet, and gold. Never before were there seen such exquisite little crawlers.

But now a sad thing happened. They were so beautiful that many creatures became their enemies, and began to kill them and eat them one after another. They crawled as fast as they could, and hid away, but many of them were killed by birds and beasts of prey, as well as by big fierce insects.

They did not know what to do, so next day the few that were left crawled back to the Grove of Ages, and once more stood before Mother Carey.

"Well, my Beauty-crawlers," she said, "what would you?"

"Oh, Mother Carey, it is fearful, everyone seeks to destroy us. Most of us are killed, and many of us wounded. Will you not protect us?"

"You drank of the two goblets, my children. I warned you that your beauty would bring terrible trouble with it."

They bowed their little heads in silent sorrow, for they knew that that was true.

"Now," said the All-Mother, "do you wish to go back and be ugly again?"

They whispered together and said: "No, Mother Carey, it is better to be beautiful and die."

Then Mother Carey looked on them very kindly, and said: "Little ones, I love your brave spirit. You shall not die. Neither shall you lose your beauty. I will give you a defence that will keep off all your enemies but one, that is the Long-stinger Wasp, for you must in some way pay for your loveliness." She waved her wand, and all over each

The Splendid Silk-Moth (about ½ life size)

of the Beauty-crawlers, there came out bunches of sharp stickers like porcupine quills, only they were worse than porcupine quills for each of the stickers was poisoned at the tip, so that no creature could touch the Beauty-crawlers without being stung.

The birds and beasts let them alone now, or suffer a terrible punishment from the poison spears. You children, too, must beware of them; touch them not, they will give you festering wounds. There is only one creature now that the Beauty-crawlers truly fear; that is the Long-stinger Wasp. He does indeed take toll of their race, but that is the price they still must pay for their beauty. Did they not drink of the double goblet?

TALE 29

The Great Splendid Silk-Moth or *Samia Cecropia*

When I was a very small boy, I saw my father bring in from the orchard a ragged looking thing like parchment wrapped up with some tangled hair; it was really the bundle-baby of this Moth. He kept it all winter, and when the spring came, I saw for the first time the great miracle of the insect world—the rag bundle was split open, and out came this glorious creature with wings of red and brown velvet, embroidered with silver and spots that looked like precious stones. It seemed the rarest thing in the world, but I have found out since, that it is one of our common moths, and any of you can get one, if you take the trouble.

Now listen, and you shall hear of what happened long ago to a green crawler who was born to be a splendid Silk-Moth, but who spoiled it all by a bad temper.

It had been a very cold, wet summer, and one day, when

the wind was whispering, he cried out: "Mother Carey, when I have done with my working life, and go into the Great Sleep, grant that it may never rain on me for I hate rain, and it has done nothing but pour all summer long." And he shivered the red knobs on his head with peevishness.

"You silly little green crawler, don't you think I know better than you what is good for you? Would you like there to be no rain?"

"Yes, I would," said the red-knobbed Samia rebelliously.

"Would *you?*" said the All-Mother to another green crawler, who hung on a near-by limb.

"Mother Carey, we have had a wet, cold summer, and the rain has been miserable, but I know you will take care of us."

"Good," said the All-Mother: "then, in this way it shall be. You little Red-Knobs shall have what you so much wish, you shall hang up in a dry loft where not a drop of dew even shall touch you in your bundle-baby sleep. And you little Yellow-Knobs shall hang under a limb where every rain that comes shall drench your outer skin." And she left them.

When the time came to hang up, Red-Knobs was led to a place as dry as could be, under a shed and swung his bundle-baby hammock from the rafters.

Yellow-Knobs hung up his hammock under a twig in the rose garden.

The winter passed, and the springtime came with the great awakening day. Each of the bundle-babies awoke from his hammock and broke his bonds. Each found his new wings, and set about shaking them out to full size and shape. Those of the rain-baby came quickly to their proper form, and away he flew to rejoice in perfect life. But though the other shook and shook, his wings would not fluff out. They seemed dried up; they were numbed and of stunted growth.

Shake as he would, the wings stayed small and twisted. And as he struggled, a Butcher-bird came by. His fierce eye was drawn by the fluttering purple thing. It had no power to escape. He tore its crumpled wings from its feathery form, and made of it a meal. But before dying it had time to say, "Oh, Mother Carey, now I know that your way was the best."

TALE 30

The Green Fairy with the Long Train

Some fairies are Brownies and some are Greenies, and of all that really and truly dance in the moonlight right here in America, Luna Greenie seems the most wonderful; and this is her history:

Once upon a time there was a seed pearl that dropped from the robe of a green fairy. It stuck on the leaf of a butternut tree till one warm day Mother Carey, who knows all the wild things and loves them all, touched it with her magic wand, called Hatch-awake, and out of the seed pearl came an extraordinarily ugly little dwarf, crawling about on many legs. He was just as greedy as he was ugly, and he ate leaf after leaf of the butternut tree, and grew so fat that he burst his skin. Then a new skin grew, and he kept on eating and bursting until he was quite big. But he had also become wise and gentle; he had learned many things, and was not quite so greedy now.

Mother Carey, the All-Mother, had been watching him, and knew that now he was ready for the next step up. She told him to make himself a hammock of rags and leaves, in the butternut tree. When he had crawled into it, she

The Green Fairy With the Long Train (about $\frac{4}{5}$ life size)

touched him with her wand, the very same as the one she used when she sent the Sleeping Beauty into her long sleep. Then that little dwarf went soundly to sleep, hanging in his hammock.

Summer passed; autumn came; the leaves fell from the butternut tree, taking the bundle-baby with them, exactly as in the old rhyme:

Rock-a-bye baby on the tree-top,
When the wind blows, your cradle will rock,
When the cold weather makes all the leaves fall,
Down tumbles baby and cradle and all.

But the hammock, with its sleeper, landed in a deep bed of leaves, and lay there all winter, quite safe and warm.

Then when the springtime sun came over the hill, Mother Carey came a-riding on the Warm Wind, and waving her wand. She stopped and kissed the sleeping bundle-baby, just as the Prince kissed the Sleeping Beauty, and instantly the baby awoke. Then happened the strangest thing. Out of that ragged old hammock there came the most wonderful and beautiful Green Fairy ever seen, with wings and with two trains; and as it came out and looked shyly around, trembling with new life, Mother Carey whispered, "Go to the butternut grove and see what awaits you there."

So away she went. Oh, how easy and glorious it is to fly! She could remember how once she used to crawl everywhere. And through the soft sweet night she flew, as she was told, straight to the butternut grove. As she came near she saw many green fairies—a great crowd of them—gathered in the moonlight, and dancing round and round in fluttering circles, swooping about and chasing each other, or hiding in the leaves. They did not feast, for these fairies never eat, and they drink only honey from flowers. But there was a spirit of great joy over them all. And there were some there with longer head plumes than those she wore. They seemed stronger and one of them came with a glad greeting to the new Green Dancer and though she flew away, she was bursting with joy that he should single her out. He pursued her till he caught her, and hand in hand they danced together in the moonlight. She was happier than she had known it was possible to be, and danced all night—that wonderful wedding dance. But she was very tired when morning was near, and high in the tree she slept so soundly that she never noticed that many seed pearls that were clustered on the lining of her robe had got loose and rolled into the crevices of the trunk. There they lay until Mother Carey came to touch them with her magic wand, so each became a crawler-dwarf, then a bundle-baby, and at last a dancing fairy.

But the Green Dancer did not know that—she knew only that it was a glorious thing to be alive, and fly, and to dance in the moonlight.

You must never fail to watch under the butternut tree on mid-summer nights, for it is quite possible that you may see the wedding dance of the Luna Greenie and her sisters with the long-trained robes.

TALE 31

The Wicked Hoptoad and the Little Yellow Dragon

ONCE upon a time, there was a beautiful little Yellow Dragon, who lived a happy and innocent life on the high banks of a prattling stream. The Dragon himself was dumb

The Wicked Hoptoad and the Little Yellow Dragon

but he loved a merry noise, and nothing pleased him more than the prattling of the water. Sometimes this pleasant little Dragon went up stream, where it was noisy, and sometimes he went down stream, where it was very silent, and rested awhile in little pools. Here it was that he met with his first enemy, a warty Hoptoad with jealous eyes. That Toad thought that he owned the pools because he bathed there every springtime, and though it was a kind little Dragon, the Toad hated him, and began to plot against him.

"Ho! little Yellow Dragon," he said, "you are very wonderful to see, and you must be very clever; but you haven't got everything you want, have you?"

The Dragon smiled, shook his head, and made silent signs with his lips. Then the Toad understood, for he said: "Ho-ho, I understand that you cannot speak. But are you happy?"

The Dragon smiled sweetly and nodded, then pointed to the stream.

That made the Toad madder than ever, for he thought it meant that the Dragon was claiming the whole stream. So the Toad said: "See, Dragon, there is a wonderful food that you have never tasted, that is a poached egg."

This he said with his heart full of guile, for he knew full well that poached eggs are deadly poison to Dragons.

The Dragon looked puzzled, and the Toad said, "Have you?"

The Dragon shook his head. "Well," said the Toad, "it is the most delicious thing in the woods; now you wait and see."

He went hoppity-hop, to a sand-bank where he had seen a Turtle lay its eggs that morning. He dug out one. He rolled it upon a stone, and split it open with the sharp spur on his heel. As soon as it was stiffened by the sun heat, he said, "Here now, Dragon, swallow it down, while I get another for myself."

The poor innocent little Dragon did not know any better. He tried to swallow the poached egg. The moment he did, it stuck in his throat, and poisoned him. At once his toes sank into the ground. He turned green all over, and his head was changed into a strange new flower. There it is to this day, standing silently where it can hear the brook a-prattling. Its body is green all over, and its head is yellow and its jaws are wide open with a poached egg stuck in its throat. And that is how it all came about. Some call it Toad Flax, and some call it Butter and Eggs, but we who know how it happened call it the Dragon and the Poached Egg.

Poor dear little Yellow Dragon!

TALE 32

The Fairy Bird or the Humming-bird Moth

WHEN I was a schoolboy, a number of my companions brought the news that the strangest bird in the world had come that day to our garden and hovered over the flowers. It was no bigger than a bumble-bee. "No! It was not a humming-bird," they said, "it was smaller by far, much more beautiful, and it came and went so fast that no one could see it go."

Every guess that I made seemed not to fit the wonderful bird, or help to give it a name that would lead us to its history in the books. The summer went by, several schoolmates saw the Wonderbird, and added stories of its marvellous smallness and mysterious habits. Its body, they said, was of green velvet with a satin-white throat; it had

The Fairy Bird (1½ life size)

a long beak—at least an inch long—a fan-tail of many feathers, two long plumes from its head, "the littlest feet you ever have seen," and large lustrous eyes that seemed filled with human intelligence. "It jest looked right at you, and seemed like a fairy looking at you."

The wonder grew. I made a sketch embodying all the points that my companions noted about the Fairy Bird. The first drawing shows what it looked like, and also gives the exact size they said it was.

It seemed a cruel wrong that let so many of them see the thing that was of chief interest to me, yet left me out. It clearly promised a real fairy, an elfin bird, a wonderful messenger from the land I hungered to believe in.

But at last my turn came. One afternoon two of the boys ran toward me, shouting: "Here it is, the little Fairy Bird, right in the garden over the honeysuckle. C'mon, quick!"

I rushed to the place, more excited than I can tell. Yes, there it was, hovering over the open flowers—tiny, wonderful, humming as it swung on misty wings. I made a quick sweep of my insect net and, marvellous to relate, scooped up the Fairy Bird. I was trembling with excitement now, not without a sense of wickedness that I should dare to net a fairy—practically an angel. But I had done it, and I gloated over my captive, in the meshes. Yes, the velvet body and snowy throat were there, the fan-tail, the plumes and the big dark eyes, but the creature was *not a bird;* it was an insect! Dimly now I remembered, and in a few hours, learned, as I had feared, that I had not captured a young angel or even a fairy—it was nothing but a Humming-bird Moth, a beautiful insect—common in some regions, scarce in some, such as mine—but perfectly well known to men of science and never afterward forgotten by any of that eager schoolboy group.

TALE 33

Ribgrass or Whiteman's-Foot

IF YOU live in the country or in a small town, you will not have to go many steps, in summer time, before you find the little plant known as Ribgrass, Plantain, or Whiteman's-foot. If you live in a big city, you may find it in any grassy place, but will surely see it, as soon as you reach the suburbs. It grows on the ground, wherever it can see the sun, and is easily known by the strong ribs, each with a string in it when you pull the leaf apart. The Indians call it Whiteman's-foot, not because it is broad and flat, but because it came from Europe with the white man; it springs up wherever he sets his foot, and it has spread over all America. Gardeners think it a troublesome weed; but the birds love its seed; canary birds delight in it; and each plant of the Ribgrass may grow many thousands of seeds in a summer.

How many? Let us see! Take a seed-stalk of the Plantain and you will find it thickly set with little cups, as in the drawing. Open one of these cups, and you find in it five seeds. Count the cups; there are two hundred on this stalk, each with about five seeds, that is, one thousand seeds; but the plant has five or more seed-stalks, some have more (one before me now has seventeen), but suppose it has only ten; then there are 10,000 seeds each summer from one little plant. Each seed can grow up into a new plant; and, if each plant were as far from the next as you can step, the little ones in a row the following summer would reach for nearly six miles; that is, from the City Hall to the end of Central Park, New York.*

*Let the Guide illustrate with some local measure.

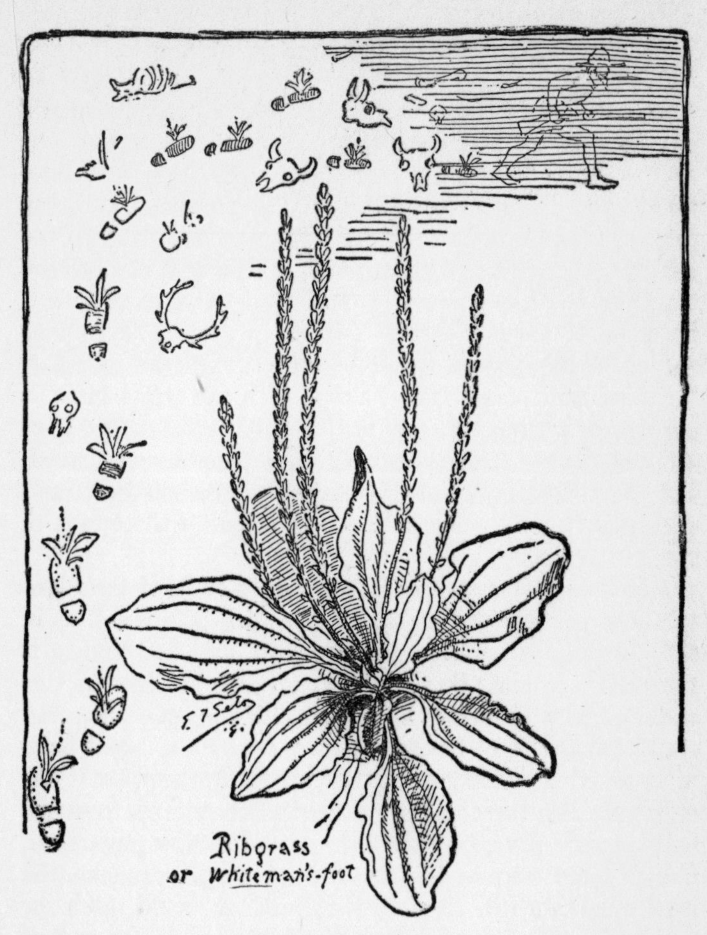

The Ribgrass

Jack-in-the-Pulpit

On the third year if all had the full number of seed, and all the seed grew into plants, there would be enough to go more than twice round the world. No wonder it has spread all over the country.

TALE 34

Jack-in-the-Pulpit

ONCE upon a time there was a missionary named the Rev. John T. Arum, who set out to preach to the Indians. He had a good heart but a bitter, biting tongue. He had no respect for the laws of the Indians, so they killed him, and buried him in the woods. But out of his grave came a new and wonderful plant, shaped like a pulpit, and right in the middle of it, as usual, was the Reverend Jack hard at it, preaching away.

If you dig down under the pulpit you will find the preacher's body, or his heart, in the form of a round root. Taste it and you will believe that the preacher had a terribly biting tongue, but treat it properly, that is boil it, and you will find out that after all he had a good little heart inside. Even the Indians have discovered his good qualities and have become very fond of him.

TALE 35

How the Indian Pipe Came

IN THE last tale you learned the fate of the Rev. John T. Arum, and the origin of Jack-in-the-Pulpit. But you must not suppose for a moment that the Indians decided in a hurry to kill the missionary. No, they had too much sense of fair play for that. They held a great many councils first to find some way of curbing his tongue, and making him mind his own business. In fact, they got into the habit

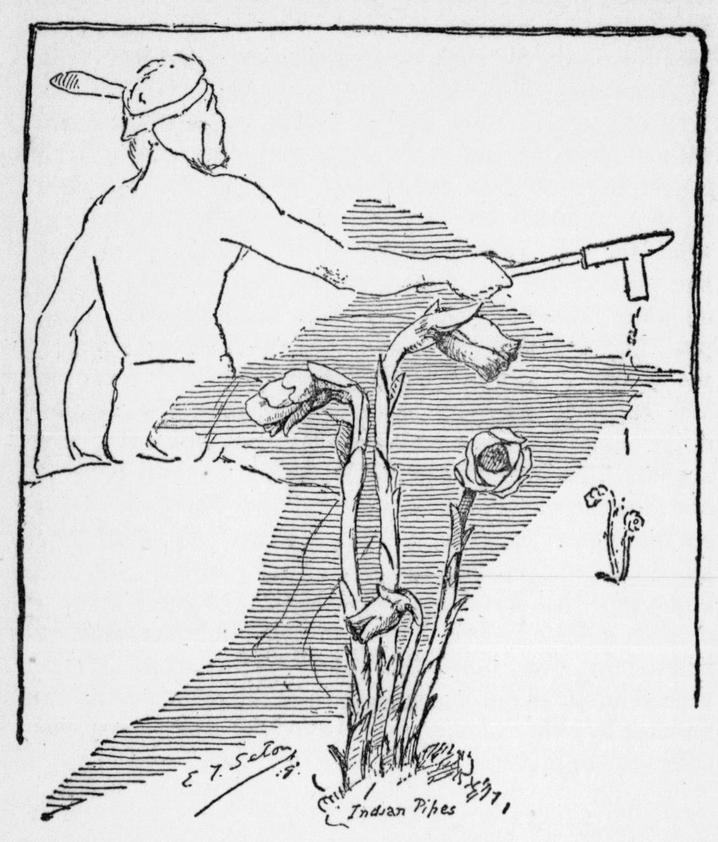

How the Indian Pipe Came

of holding a council every few minutes to discuss the question, no matter where they were or what else they were doing. So that pretty nearly every part of the woods was in time used for a council ring to discuss the fate of the Rev. John T. Arum.

Of course, you know that no Indian can hold a council without smoking the Peace Pipe, and when the council is over, he empties out the ashes of the pipe. So that when all those councils were over, when the matter was settled, when the missionary was buried, and when the warrior had gone to the ghost land, there came solemnly poking its white bowl and stem from under the leaves an Indian pipe, at the very spot where the Councillors had emptied the ashes. It is a beautifully shaped pipe, with a curved and feathered stem, but it has none of the bright colours of the old Peace Pipe. It cannot have them for this is only a ghost Pipe to show where the council used to be; and one pipe there is for each council held on that spot, so you see how many, many councils the Indians had, before they killed the troublesome preacher. And sometimes you can find a pipe that has the bowl still filled with ghost tobacco or even a little red ghost fire, showing that the warriors had to hurry away before that council was finished. Whenever you find the ghost pipe in the woods, you are sure to see close by either a log, a bank or a rock on which the Councillors sat to talk it over.

TALE 36

The Cucumber Under the Brownie's Umbrella

THE Indians had Brownies, only they called them Pukwudjies, and I am going to tell you a story of an Indian Brownie.

Whenever the Indians got together for a council, the

The Cucumber Under the Brownie's Umbrella

Brownies did the same thing, in the woods near by. It was a kind of Brownie Fair, and some of the little people used to have stands and sell refreshments. Berries were scarce in the springtime, but the Brownies were very fond of cucumber. So there were always one or two Cucumber Brownies, who set up their little umbrellas, and sold slices of Cucumber to the others.

When it was time to go home, or when the sun got so hot that the cucumbers were likely to spoil, they would bury them in the ground, but leave the umbrella to mark the place. And there they are yet; many a time have I found the umbrella, and dug under it to find the cucumber. It is delicious eating; everything that Brownies like is. You can find it, and try it. It is one of the things that Monapini taught Ruth Pilgrim to eat. (Tale 18).

Of course, the Brownies do not like you to dig up their treasure or good-to-eats, but there are plenty more, far more than they ever need. "Yet what about it," you say, "if the Brownie happens to be there?"

He may be sitting right under the umbrella, but remember the little people are invisible to our eyes. You will not see him; at least I never did.

TALE 37

The Hickory Horn-devil

HUSH, whisper! Did you ever meet a Hickory Horn-devil? No! Well I did, and I tell you he is a terror. Look at this picture of him. It is true, only he is not quite so big as that, though he looks as if he might be. And I was not quite so small as that, only I felt as if I were! And everything about him looked horribly strong, poisonous and ugly. He was a real devil.

The Hickory Horn-devil (½ life size)

I did not know his history then; I did not learn it for a long time after, but I can tell it to you now.

Once upon a time there was a little, greenish, blackish worm. He loved pretty things, and he hated to be ugly, as he was. No one wanted him, and he was left all alone, a miserable little outcast. He complained bitterly to Mother Carey, and asked if she would not bless him with some grace, to help him in his troubles.

Mother Carey said: "Little ugly worm; you are having a hard time, because in your other life, before you came into this shape, you had an ugly, hateful spirit. You must go through this one as you are, until the Great Sleep comes; after that, you will be exactly what you have made of yourself."

Then the little ugly worm said: "Oh Mother Carey, I am as miserable as I can be; let me be twice as ugly, if, in the end, I may be twice as beautiful."

Mother Carey said gravely, "Do you think you could stand it, little worm? We shall see."

From that time the worm got bigger and uglier, no creature would even talk to him. The birds seemed to fear him, and the Squirrels puffed out little horror-snorts, when they saw him coming, even the other worms kept away from him.

So he went on his lonely life, uglier and more hated than ever. He lived chiefly on a big hickory tree, so men called him the Hickory Horn-devil.

One day as he was crawling on a fence, a hen with chickens came running after him, to eat him. But when she saw how ugly he was she cried: "Oh, Lawk, lawk! Come away, children, at once!"

At another time he saw a Chipmunk teaching its little ones to play tag. They looked so bright and happy, he longed, not to join them because he could only crawl, but to have the happiness of looking on. But when he came slowly forward, and the old Chipmunk saw him waving his horns and looking like a green poisonous reptile, she screamed, "Run, my children!" and all darted into their hole while Mother Chipmunk stuffed up the doorway with earth.

But the most thrilling thing of all that he saw was one day as the sun went down, a winged being of dazzling beauty alighted for a moment on his hickory tree. Never had the Horn-devil seen such a dream of loveliness. Her slender body was clad in rose velvet, and her wings were shining with gold. The very sight of her made him hate himself, yet he could not resist the impulse to crawl nearer, to gaze at her beauty.

But her eyes rested a moment on his horrible shape, and she fled in fear, while a voice near by said: "The Spangled Queen does not love poisonous reptiles." Then the poor little Horn-devil wished he were dead. He hid away from sight for three days. Hunger however forced him out, and as he was crawling across a pathway, a man who came along was going to crush him underfoot, but Mother Carey whispered, "No, don't do it." So the man let him live, but roughly kicked the worm aside, and bruised him fearfully.

Then came Mother Carey and said: "Well, little ugly worm! Is your spirit strong, or angry?"

The worm said bravely, though feebly: "Mother, Mother Carey, I am trying to be strong. I want to win."

The breezes were losing their gentle warmth when Mother Carey came to him one day, and said: "Little one, your trial has been long, but it is nearly over.

"Prepare to sleep now, my little horny one, you have fought a brave fight; your reward is coming. Because your soul has been made beautiful by your suffering, I will give you a body blazing with such beauty as shall make all stand in adoration when you pass." Then Mother Earth said, "Our little one shall have extra care because he has had extra trials." So the tired little Horn-devil did not even have to make himself a hammock, for Mother Earth received him and he snuggled into her bosom. As Mother Carey waved her wand, he dropped off asleep. And he slept for two hundred days.

Then came the great Awakening Day, the resurrection day of the woods. Many new birds arrived. Many new flowers appeared. Sleepers woke from underground, as Mother Carey's silent trumpeters went bugling ahead of her, and her winged horse, the Warm Wind, came sweeping across the meadows, with the white world greening as he came.

The bundle-baby of the Horn-devil woke up. He was cramped and sleepy, but soon awake. Then he knew that he was a prisoner, bound up in silken cords of strength. But new powers were his now, he was able to break the cords and crawl out of his hole. He put up his feelers to find those horrible horns, but they were gone, and his devil form fell off him like a mask. He had wings, jewelled wings! on his back now. Out he came to fluff the new-found wings awhile, and when they were spread and supple he flew into the joyful night, one of the noblest of all the things that fly, gorgeous in gold and velvet, body and wings; filled with the joy of life and flight, he went careering through the soft splendour of the coming night. And as he flew, he glimpsed a radiant form ahead, a being like himself, with wings of velvet and gold. At first he thought it was the Princess of the Hickory Tree, but now his eyes were perfect, and he could see that this was a younger and more beautiful Spangled Princess than the one of his bygone life, and all his heart was filled with the blazing fire of love.

Fearlessly now he flew to overtake her; for was she not of his own kind? She sped away, very fast at first, but maybe she did not go as fast as she could, for soon he was sailing by her side. At first she turned away a little, but she was not cross or frightened now. She was indeed inclined to play and tease. Then in their own language, he asked her to marry him, and in their own language she said, "yes." Away they flew and flew on their wedding flight, high in the trees in the purple night, glorious in velvet and gold, more happy than these printed words can tell.

The wise men who saw them said, "There go the Royal Citheronia and his bride." And Mother Carey smiled as she saw their bliss, and remembered the Hickory Horn-devil.

THINGS TO SEE IN AUTUMNTIME

The Purple and Gold of Autumn

Things to See in Autumntime

TALE 38

The Purple and Gold of Autumn

THERE was once an old gentleman named Father Time, and he had four beautiful daughters.

The eldest was called Winter Time. She was tall and pale. She dressed chiefly in white wool trimmed with wonderful lacework. She was much admired by some, but others considered her very cold and distant. And most agreed that she was the least winsome of the sisters.

The second one was called Spring Time, and she was dressed in beautiful golden-green satin. She had a gentle, sunny disposition; some thought her the loveliest.

The third was Summer Time, and her robe was dark-green velvet. She was warm-hearted and most attractive, full of life and energy, and as unlike the eldest sister as possible.

The youngest was Autumn Time. She certainly was a wonderful creature, with red rosy cheeks, plump form, and riotous good spirits. Her robes were gorgeous and a little extravagant, for she wore a new one every day, and of all that she had, the one that she loved the best and wore the latest was of purple and gold. We can go out in October and see the purple and gold, and gather some scraps of the robe, for it is on every wayside and every hillside.

TALE 39

Why the Chicadee Goes Crazy Twice a Year

A LONG time ago, when it was always summer in our woods, the Chicadees lived merrily with their cousins, and frolicked the whole year round. But one day Mother Carey sent the small birds a warning that they must move to the South, when the leaves fell from the trees, for hard frost and snow were coming, and maybe starvation too.

All the cousins of the Chicadees listened to the warning and got ready to go; but Tomtit, their leader, only laughed and turned a dozen wheels around a twig that served him for a bar.

"Go to the South?" said he. "Not I; I am too happy here; and as for frost and snow, I never saw any, and I don't believe there are such things."

Very soon the leaves fell from the trees and the Nuthatches and the King-wrens were so busy getting ready to go that the Chicadees left off play for a minute, to ask questions. They were not pleased with the answer they got, for the messenger had said that all of them were to take a long, long journey that would last for days, and the little King-wrens had actually to go as far as the Gulf of Mexico. Besides, they were to fly by night, to avoid their enemies, the Hawks, and the weather at this season was sure to be stormy. So the Chicadees said it was all nonsense, and went off, singing and chasing one another through the woods, led by Tomtit singing a new song in which he made fun of the travellers.

Tom Tom Tiddy-Mouse!
Hid away in our house,
Hid his brother in the cellar.
Wasn't he a silly feller?

But their cousins were quite serious. They picked out wise leaders and formed themselves into bands. They learned that they must follow their leader, they must twitter as they flew in the darkness, so as to let those behind know where the leaders were; they must follow the great rivers southward; they must wait for a full moon before starting, and never travel by day.

The noisy, rollicking Chicadees continued to make fun of their cousins as they saw them now gathering in the woods along the river; and at length, when the moon was big, bright, and full, the cousins arose to the call of the leaders and all flew away in the gloom. The Chicadees said that all the cousins were crazy, made some good jokes about the Gulf of Mexico, and then dashed away on their favourite game of tag and tumble through the woods, which, however, did seem rather quiet now, and bare of leaves; while the weather, too, was certainly turning uncomfortably cool.

At length the frost and snow really did come, and the Chicadees were in a bad way. Indeed, they were frightened out of their wits, and dashed hither and thither, seeking in vain for some one to set them aright on the way to the warm land. They flew wildly about the woods, till they were truly crazy. I suppose there was not a squirrel-hole or a hollow log in the neighbourhood that some Chicadee did not enter to inquire if this was the Gulf of Mexico. But no one could tell anything about it, no one was going that way, and the great river was hidden under ice and snow.

About this time a messenger from Mother Carey was passing with a message to the Caribou in the Far North; but all he could tell the Chicadees was that he could not be their guide, as he had other business. "Besides," he said, "you had the same notice as your cousins whom you called 'crazy.' And from what I know of Mother Carey, you will probably have to stick it out here all through the snow, not only now, but in every winter after this; so you may as well make the best of it."

This was sad news for the Chicadee Tomtits; but they were brave little fellows, and seeing they could not help themselves, they went about making the best of it. Before a week had gone by they were in their usual good spirits again, scrambling about the snowy twigs, or chasing one another as before.

They were glad to remember now that Mother Carey said that winter would end. They told each other about it so much that even at its beginning, when a fresh blizzard came on, they would gleefully remark to one another that it was a "sign of spring," and one or another of the flock would lift his voice in the sweet little chant that we all know so well:

Spring soon

Another would take it up and answer back:

Spring com - ing

and they would keep on repeating the song until the dreary woods rang again with the good news, and the wood-people learned to love the brave little bird that sets his face so cheerfully, to meet so hard a case.

And winter did end. Spring did come at last. And the sign of its coming was when the ice broke on the stream and the pussy willow came purring out above it. The air was full of the good news. The Chicadees felt it, and knew it through and through. They went mad with joy, chasing each other round and round the trees and through the hollow logs, shouting "The spring is here, the spring is here, Hurree, Hurree, Hurree," and in another week their joyous lives were going on as before the trouble came.

But to this day, when the chill wind blows through the deserted woods, the Chicadees seem to lose their wits for a few days, and dart into all sorts of queer places. They may then be found in great cities, or open prairies, cellars, chimneys, and hollow logs; and the next time you find one of the wanderers in any out-of-the-way corner, be sure to remember that the Chicadee goes crazy twice a year, in the fall and in the spring, and probably went into his strange hole or town in search of the Gulf of Mexico.

TALE 40

The Story of the Quaking Aspen or Poplar

THE leaf of the Quaking Asp is like the one marked "a" in the drawing. Its trunk is smooth, greenish, or whitish, with black knots of bark like "c". All the farmers know it as Popple, or White Poplar; but the hunters call it Quaking Asp or Aspen.

The name "quaking" was given because it is for ever shaking its leaves; the slightest wind sets them all rustling. They move so easily because each leaf-stem is like a thin,

The Story of the Quaking Aspen

flat strap set on edge; while the leaf-stem of such as the oak is nearly round and scarcely rustles at all. Why does the Quaking Asp do this? No doubt, because it lives in places where the hot dust falls thick on the leaves at times, and if it did not have some trick of shaking it off, the leaf would be choked and bent so that the tree could scarcely breathe; for the leaves are the lungs of the trees. So remember, when the Poplar rustles loudly, it is coughing to clear its lungs of the dust.

Some trees try to hide their troubles, and quickly cover up their wounds; but the Aspen has a very touchy skin and, once it is wounded, it shows the scar as long as it lives. We can, therefore, go to any Aspen tree, and have it tell us the story of its life. Here is the picture of one. The black marks at the forks (c) are scars of growth; the belts of dots (d) were wounds given by a sapsucker to rob it of its sap; the flat places (e) show where a Red Squirrel gnawed off the outer bark.

If a Raccoon climbed the tree (f), or an insect bored into the trunk, we are sure to see a record of it in this sensitive bark.

Now, last of all, the paper on which this story is printed was likely made out of Aspen wood.

TALE 41

The Witch-hazel

THESE are the things to make you remember the Witch-hazel; its forked twig was used—nay, still is used—as a magic rod to show where there is running water underground; that is, where it is possible to find water by sinking a well. Its nuts are explosive, and go off with a *snap*, shooting the seeds that are inside. ten or twenty feet away,

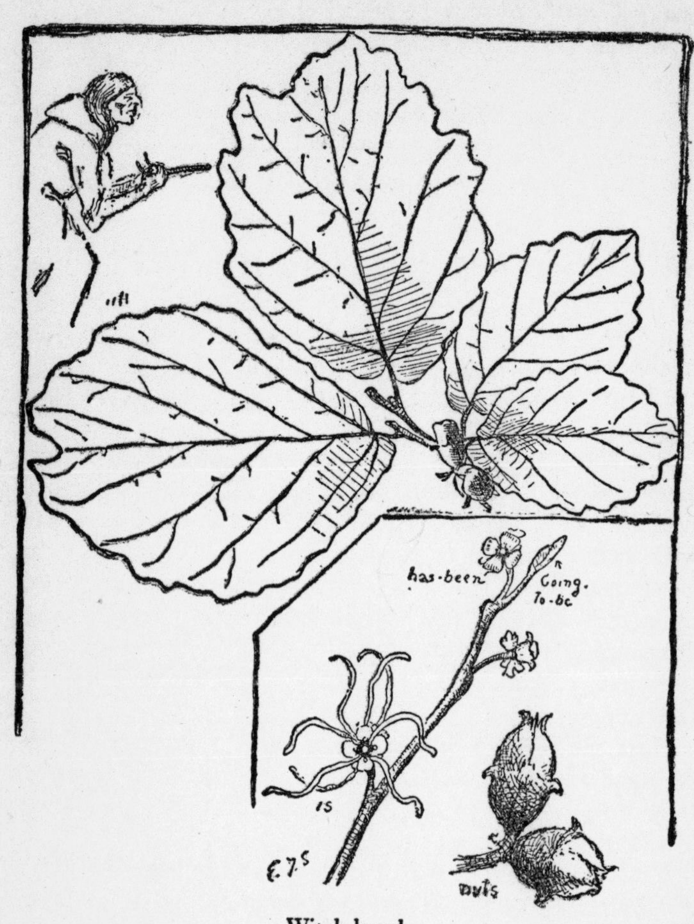

Witch-hazel

when the cold dry days of autumn come. Third, its curious golden-thread flowers appear in the fall.

As Cracked Jimmy used to sing:-

> Witch-hazel blossoms in the fall,
> To cure the chills and fevers all.
> —*Two Little Savages.*

On November 16, 1919, after a sharp frost, I went out in the morning to get some Witch-hazel flowers for this drawing, and found them blooming away in the cold air, vigorously as ever. Imagine a flower that can bloom while it is freezing. In the drawing I have shown the flower, like a 4-lipped cup with four yellow snakes coiling out of it.

But these are not the deadly snakes one hears about. They are rather symbols of old Æsculapius, the famous healer of the long ago, whose emblem was the cup of life with curling snakes of wisdom about it. In the Witch-hazel has been found a soothing balm for many an ache and pain. The Witch-hazel you buy in the drugstores, is made out of the bark of this tree. If you chew one of the little branches you will know it by the taste.

Near the top is a flower that is finished, its snakes have fled; and at the top of all is a bud for next year. That is, they are—*is*, *has-been* and *going-to-be*. The nuts are shown in the corner.

Note, last of all, that it is a sociable little tree; it always goes with a crowd. There are generally three or four Witch-hazels from one root, and there is always a family of cousins not far away.

TALE 42

How the Shad Came and How the Chestnut Got Its Burrs

IN THE woods of Poconic there once roamed a very discontented Porcupine. She was forever fretting. She complained that everything was wrong, till it was perfectly scandalous, and Wahkonda, the Great Spirit, getting tired of her grumbling, said:

"You and the world I have made don't seem to fit; one or the other must be wrong. It is easier to change you. You don't like the trees, you are unhappy on the ground, and think everything is upside down, therefore I'll turn you inside out, and put you in the water." And so the Porcupine was turned into a new creature, a fish, called the Shad. That is why he is so full of little sharp bones.

Then after the old Porcupine had been turned into a Shad, the young ones missed their mother, and crawled up into a high Chestnut tree to look for her coming. Wahkonda happened to pass that way, and they all chattered their teeth at him, thinking themselves safe. They were not wicked, but at heart quite good, only badly brought up; oh, so ill-trained, and some of them chattered and groaned as Wahkonda came nearer. Then Wahkonda was sorry for them, remembering that he had taken their mother from them, and said: "You look very well up there, you little Porkys, so you had better stay there for always, and be part of the Chestnut tree." And he touched each one with his magic wand and turned it into a burr that grew tight to the tree. That is how it came about. There they hang like a lot of little Porcupines on the twigs of the tree. They are spiney and dangerous, utterly without manners, and yet most of them have a good little heart inside.

TALE 43

How the Littlest Owl Came

AFTER the Great Spirit had made the world and the creatures in it, he made the Gitchee O-kok-o-hoo. This was like an Owl, but bigger than anything else alive, and his voice was like a river plunging over a rocky ledge. He was so big that he thought he had done it all himself, and he became puffed up. He forgot the Great Spirit, who decided to teach him a lesson in this wise:

He called the Blue-jay, the mischief-maker of the woods, and told him what to do. Away went the Blue-jay to the mountain at the top of which was the Gitchee O-kok-o-hoo making thunder in his throat. The Blue-jay flew up to his ear, and said: "Pooh, Gitchee O-kok-o-hoo, you don't call that a big noise! You should hear Niagara; then you would never twitter again."

The Gitchee O-kok-o-hoo was so mad at hearing his big wonderful song called a twitter, that he said: "Niagara, Niagara! I'm sick of hearing about Niagara. I will go and silence Niagara with my voice." So he flew to Niagara while the Blue-jay snickered and followed to see the fun.

Now when Niagara Falls was made the Great Spirit said to it, "Flow on for ever." That last word of the Great Spirit it took up as it rushed on, and never ceases to thunder out "For ever! For ever! For ever!'

When they came to Niagara the mighty cataract, the Blue-jay said, "Now, Gitchee, you can beat that I am sure." So Gitchee O-kok-o-hoo began bawling to drown the noise of it, but could not make himself heard.

"Wa-wa-wa," said the Gitchee O-kok-o-hoo, with great effort and only for a few heart beats.

"*For ever, For ever, For ever,*" thundered the river, steadily, easily, ceaselessly.

"Wa-wa-wa—!" shrieked Gitchee O-kok-o-hoo; but his voice was so utterly lost that he could not hear it himself, and he began to feel small, and smaller; and as he began to feel small, a strange thing happened—he began to get small and smaller, until he was no bigger than a Sparrow; and his voice, instead of being like a great cataract, became like the dropping of water, just a little

Tink-tank-tink,
Tink-tank-tink.

And this is why the Indians give to this smallest of the Owls the name of "The Water-dropping Bird," who was once the greatest of all creatures, but is now shrunk to be the littlest of the Owls, because he became proud and forgot the Great Spirit.

TALE 44

The Wood-witch and the Bog-nuts

ONCE upon a time there was a rich boy, who knew all about the city, and nothing about the woods. He went for an outing into the wilderness, and got lost. He wandered all day until he was very tired and hungry. The sun was low when he came to a little pathway. He followed it, and it led to a small log cabin. When he knocked, an old woman opened the door. He said, "Please, Ma'am, I am lost and very hungry, will you give me something to eat?"

The old woman looked sharply at his clothes, and knew

The Wood-witch and the Bog-nuts

that he was rich, so she said: "Poor people are wise, they can take care of themselves in the woods. They don't get lost. But you rich people are fools, and I wish you would go away."

"I will, if you'll give me something to eat," he answered.

Then the old woman said: "Listen, foolish rich boy, in the woods beside you right now is a friend who feeds the poor people, maybe she will feed you. She is tall and slim, her eyes are brownish purple and her hair is green, and by this you may know her—she has five fingers on one hand and seven on the other. Her house is in the brier thicket; she climbs to the roof and stands there all day waving her hands, and shouting out in wood-talk, 'There are cocoanuts in my cellar.'

"Now go and find her, maybe she will feed you. She always feeds us poor folks," and the witch slammed the door.

The boy was puzzled. As he stood in doubt, there was a loud noise, and his friends arrived. They brought him the food and comfort that he needed.

Then he said: "I wish to know what that old wood-witch meant by the lady with the purple eyes and green hair." So he went again to the log cabin and knocked.

When the old woman came, and saw a lot of people about, she was frightened for she knew she had been unkind. But the boy said: "Now Granny, you needn't be afraid, I want you to show me the friend that has seven fingers and a cellar full of cocoanuts."

"I'll show you, if you promise to do me no harm," she answered.

"Of course, I'll promise," replied the boy.

Then Granny Wood-witch went hobbling to the nearest thicket and cackled out loud, as she pointed out a trailing vine that had sometimes five leaflets on a stalk and sometimes seven. "See, see, that's the lady. See seven fingers on that hand and five on this. Now follow her feet down and dig in the ground."

They dug and found strings of lovely brown nuts as big as walnuts.

"See, see," chuckled the wood-witch. "See the cocoanuts in the cellar."

Go forth and look for it, ye Woodcrafters. You will find it throughout Eastern America on the edge of every wood. Its flower is like a purple-brown sweet-pea, and is in bloom all summer long. Follow down its vine, dig out a few of the potatoes or nuts, and try them, raw, boiled, or if ye wish to eat them as Indian Cake, clean them, cut them in slices, dry till hard, pound them up into meal, and make a cake the same as you would of oatmeal.

The wild things love them, the Indians love them, and this was the bread of the wood-witch. The books call it Bog Potato and Ground Nuts. It is the third secret of the woods.

TALE 45

The Mud-dauber Wasp

If you look under the roof of any wooden barn in Eastern America you are likely to see the nest of the common Mud-wasp.

If you look on warm sunny days along the edge of some mud puddle you are sure to see a curious steel-blue wasp, with a very thin waist, working away at a lump of mud. She seems to be breathing hard with her body, as she works with her yellow legs, but she finally goes off laden with a gob of mud. This is the Mud-wasp at work, building a strong mud-nest for her family. The nest is the one we

The Mud-dauber Wasp (life size)

have seen hung under the roof of the shed, always put where no rain can reach it.

In the drawing are two of these nests.

Once the cradle is ready, the mother Wasp goes spider-hunting. Whenever she can find a spider, she pounces on it, and with her sting, she stabs it in the body, so as to paralyze it, but not kill it. Then she carries it to the mud cell and packs it in, at the far end. Many spiders are caught and preserved this way, for they do not usually die though they cannot move.

When the cell is full, the Wasp lays an egg on the last spider, and seals up the opening with a mud lid.

Very soon the egg hatches out a little white grub which begins on the spider next to him, eating the legs first, and the body last, so as to keep it alive as long as possible, though of course the spider has no feeling. Then he eats the next spider, and the next, growing as he eats, until he nearly fills the cell, and the spiders are all eaten up.

Now the grub goes to sleep, and next spring comes out as a full-grown Mud-wasp to do exactly as the mother did, though it never saw that Mother or had a lesson from any one in the many strange things it must do to live.

I went into my boat-house to-day, November 20, 1919, to get a mud nest for this drawing. There were 86 on the roof; some of them with 20 or 30 cells, and besides there was a lot of paper nests by other Wasps. The nest I took had two cells, one open and empty, and the other with a mud lid on tight. This held a long, shiny brown transparent case, in which was a white grub much too small for the big coat he was wearing. The grub was sound asleep, and would have come out next spring, as a big steel-blue Mud-wasp had I let him alone. But there are plenty of Mud-wasps so I fed him to the Chicadees, which likely is what Mother Carey would have done.

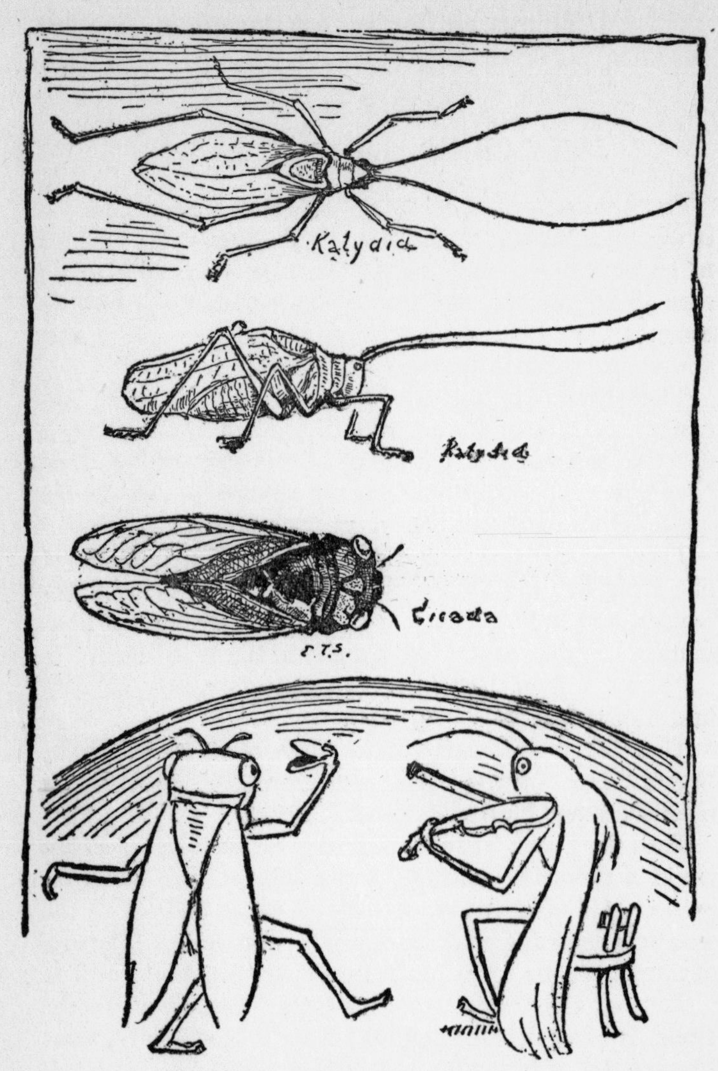

The Cicada and the Katydid (life size)

TALE 46

The Cicada and the Katydid

ONCE upon a time, long, long ago, the birds whose job it was to make the woods merry with their songs, decided to go on strike. They said, "We have sung all day, all springtime, and half way through the summer, but now we are moulting, the weather is frightfully hot; we need a rest, and we are going to stop singing, to take a holiday."

Then Dame Nature, who is sometimes called the All-mother, or Mother Carey, said: "Dear me, this will never do! No songbirds, woods silent all through the dog-days. Now who will be strike-breakers and volunteer to supply the music till the birds get once more in a good humour?"

Then up at that question got a long-winged insect like a big fly, and a long-legged insect like a green grass-hopper, and both said at once, "I will." Amid low murmurs of "Scab! Scab!" from many of the Wood-birds.

"You. I forgot that you two had any voices at all!" said Mother Carey.

Then the long-winged creature, whose name is Cicada, began, "True, my voice isn't much, but I have invented a most successful musical castanet. Listen!"

Then he began an extraordinary racket like an alarm clock, a threshing machine, and a buzz-saw all going together. He filled the grove with his noise, and set all the woodfolk laughing with his funny performance. Though, of course, he didn't mean to be funny; he thought it was fine.

Then as the Cicada ceased, Mother Carey said to the Green Hopper, whose name was Katy, "Now, Katy, what can you do?

"I do not brag of my voice, dear Mother," said she, "but I am a thrilling performer on the violin."

Then she humped herself up over a green fiddle that she had under her cloak, and nearly deafened them with its hoarse screechings.

There was no doubt that these two could make as much noise as a wood full of birds; both were eager to take sole charge, and a bitter dispute arose as to whose idea it was first.

But Mother Carey settled it by dividing the time. "You," she said to Cicada, "can take charge of the music by day, and you," she said to the Green one, "must take it up at sundown in place of the nightingale, and keep it up, till the night breaks, and both of you continue till the frost comes, or until the birds are back on the job."

That is how it all came about.

But there is considerable feeling yet among the Katies, that they should get all the night work, and never be seen performing. They think that their ancestor was the original inventor of this cheap substitute for bird song. And it is made all the worse by a division among themselves. Some say "she did" and some say "she didn't." If you notice in early August, they are nearly all shouting, "Katy-did." Then by the end of the month, "Katy-didn't" is stronger. In September it is still mixed. In October their work is over, the chorus ended, but you hear an occasional "Katy-did" and finally as late as Indian Summer, which is Hallowe'en, I have heard the last of the fiddlers rasp out "she did"; and do it in daytime, too, as though to flout the followers of Cicada. And, if the last word be truth, as they say, we may consider it settled, that Katy really and truly *did*. And yet I believe next year the same dispute will arise, and we shall have the noisy argument all over again.

If you look at the portraits of Cicada, the Hotweather-bug or Locust, and of the Katydid, you will not see their musical instruments very plainly, but believe me they have them; and you can hear them any late summer hot-weather time, in any part of the Eastern States and some parts of southern Canada.

And now let me finish with a secret. Katy is not a lady at all, but a he-one disguised in green silk stockings, and a green satin dress.

TALE 47

The Digger Wasp that Killed the Cicada

STRANGE things are done in the realm of Mother Carey; strange things and cruel. At least so they seem to us, for we do not know the plan that is behind them. We know only that sometimes love must be cruel. I am going to tell you of a strange happening, that you may see any hot day in August. And this is how it came about.

At that meeting in the woods when the Cicada and the Katydid undertook to be musicians, while the birds were on strike, there was one strong insect who gave off an angry "*Bizz, Bizz*" that sounded like "*Scab, Scab.*" That was the big yellow-and-black Digger Wasp, the biggest of the wasps, with a sting that is as bad as that of a baby rattle-snake. And that very day she declared war on the Cicada and his kind. The Katydids she could not touch, because the Wasp cannot see at night.

But the Cicada was easy to find. As soon as the day got hot, and that awful buzzing began in the trees, the Big Digger got her sting ready, and went booming along in the direction of the sound.

Now Mother Carey had given the Cicada bright eyes and strong wings, and it was his own business to take care of himself; but he was so pleased with his music that he never saw the fierce Digger Wasp, till she charged on him.

The Digger Wasp (life size)

And before he could spread his wings, she had stabbed him through.

His song died away in a few shrieks, and then the Cicada lay still. But not dead, for the Digger had stuck her poison dagger into the nerve centre, so that he was paralyzed and helpless, but still living.

Now the Digger set about a plan. She wanted to get that Cicada body into her den, to feed her young ones with it. But the Cicada was bigger and heavier than she was, so that she could not carry it. However, she was bent on doing it, she got all ready, took tight hold with her claws, then swooped from the tree, flying as strongly as she could, till the weight of the Cicada brought her to the ground within fifty feet, while the den was fully a hundred feet away. But the Wasp dragged the Cicada up the trunk of another tree, then took another long sloping flight as before. One more climb and skid down, brought her to her den—a hole in a bank that she had dug out; that is why she is called the Digger Wasp. The passage was a foot long and had a crook in the middle. At the end was a round room an inch and a half high. Here the Digger left her victim's body and right on its breast, to one side, laid an egg.

This hatched in two or three days, and began to feed on the Cicada. In a week it had eaten the Cicada and grown to be a big fat grub. Then it spun a cocoon, and made itself into a bundle-baby, resting all autumn and all winter in that dark den.

But when the spring came with its glorious wakening up, great changes came over the bundle-baby of the Digger. It threw off the cocoon and its outer skin, and came forth from the gloom into the sunshine, a big strong Digger Wasp with a sting of its own, and a deadly feud with all screaming Cicadas. Although it never saw its mother, or got any lessons from her, it goes after the buzzing hotweather-bugs, when August comes, and treats them exactly as she did.

TALE 48

How the Indian Summer Came

WAHKONDA, the Great Spirit, the Ruler of the World, had found pleasure the whole summer long in making mountains, lakes, and forests. Then when the autumn came, and the leaves fell from the trees, He lighted His pipe and sat down to look over the things He had made.

As He did so, the north wind arose for Cold Time was coming, and blew the smoke and ashes of the pipe into His face. Then He said: "Cease your blowing, all ye winds, until I have finished smoking." So, of course, there was dead calm.

Wahkonda smoked for ten days, and during all that time there were no clouds in the sky, for there was no wind to bring them; there was unbroken, calm sunny weather. But neither was there any wind to carry off the smoke, so it hung, as the teepee smoke hangs at sunrise, and it drifted over the valleys and forests in a blue haze.

Then at last when the Great Spirit finished His smoke and His meditation, He emptied out His pipe. That was the signal, the north wind broke loose, and came howling down from the hills, driving the leaves before it, and warning all wild things to be ready, for soon there would be winter in the woods.

And it hath been so ever since. When the leaves have fallen and before yet the Ice-king is here, there come, for a little while, the calm dreamy days, when the Great Spirit is smoking His pipe, and the smoke is on the land. The Red-men call them the Smoking Days, but we call it Indian Summer.

THINGS TO SEE IN WINTERTIME

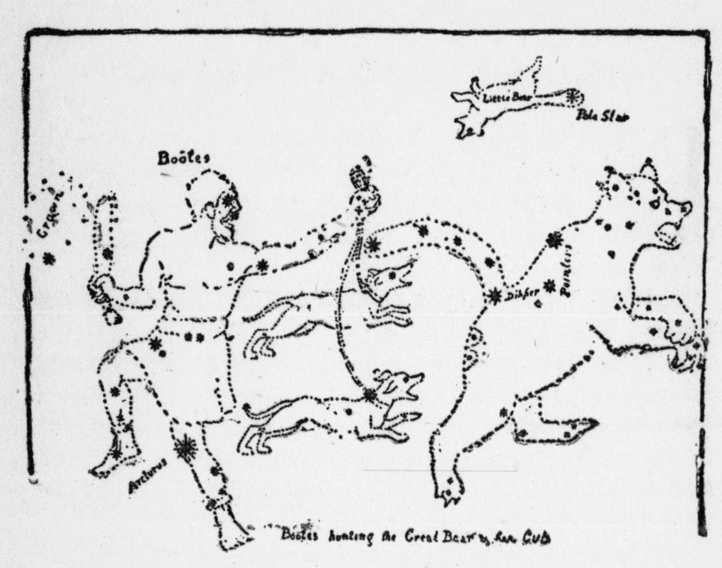

The North Star or Home Star

Things to See in Wintertime

TALE 49

The North Star, or the Home Star

IF YOU are going to be a Woodcrafter, you must begin by knowing the North Star, because that is the star which will show you the way home, if you get lost in the woods at night. That is why the Indians call it the "Home Star."

But first, I must tell you how it came to be, and the story begins a long, long time ago.

In those far-off days, we are told, there were two wonderful hunters, one named Orion, and the other named Boötes (Bo-o-tees). Orion hunted everything and I shall have to leave him for another story. Boötes was an ox-driver and only hunted bears to save his cattle. One day he went after a Mother Bear, that had one little cub.

He chased them up to the top of a mountain so high, that they leaped off into the sky, and just as they were going, Boötes shot his arrows after them. His very first arrow hit the Little Bear in the tail—they had long tails in those days—and pinned him to the sky. There he has hung ever since, swinging round and round, on the arrow in his tail, while his mother runs bawling around him, with Boötes and his dogs chasing her. He shot arrows into her tail, which was long and curved, into her body, and into her shoulder. Seven big arrows he shot, and there they are yet,

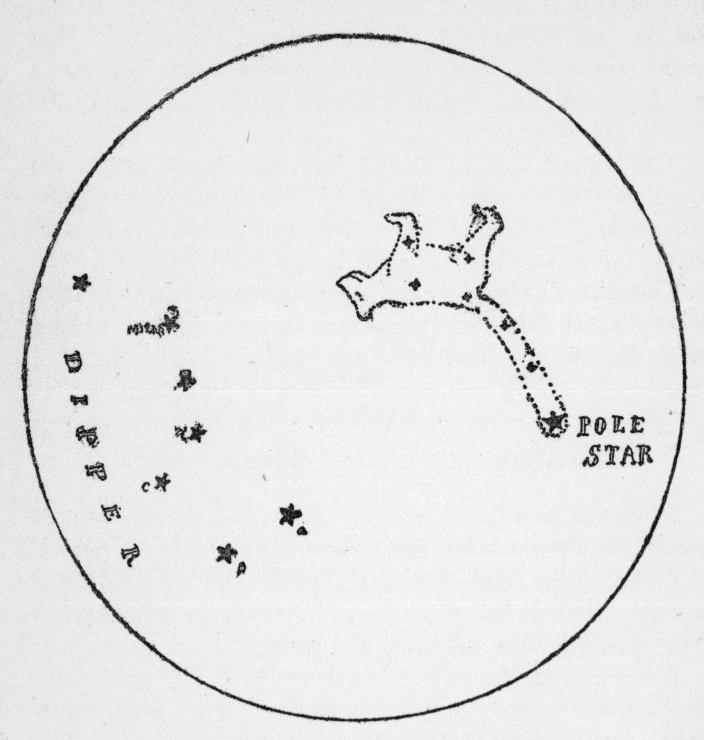

The Pappoose on the Squaw's Back

in the form of a dipper pointing always to the cub who is called the "Little Bear." The shining head of the big arrow in the end of the Little Bear's tail is called the North Star or Pole Star. You can always tell which is the North Star, by the two Pointers; these are the two bright stars that make the outer side of the Dipper on the Big Bear's shoulder. A line drawn through them, points out the North Star.

The Dipper, that is the Big Bear, goes round and round the Pole Star, once in about twenty-four hours; so that sometimes the Pointers are over, sometimes under, to left or to right; but always pointing out the Pole Star or North Star.

This star shows nearly the true north; and, knowing that, a traveller can find his way in any strange country, so long as he can see this friendly Home Star.

TALE 50

The Pappoose on the Squaw's Back

Now that you know how the Bears and the Big Dipper came, you should know the Indian story of the Old Squaw.

First find the bright star that is at the bend of the Dipper handle. This is called the "Old Squaw"; on her back is a tiny star that they call "The Pappoose."

As soon as an Indian boy is old enough to understand, his mother takes him out into the night when it is calm and clear, and without any moon or any bright lights near, and says, "My child, yonder is the Old Squaw, the second of the seven stars; she is going over the top of the hill; on her back she carries her pappoose. Tell me, my child, can you see the pappoose?"

Then the little redskin gazes, and from his mother's hand he takes two pebbles, a big one and a little one, and he sets them together on her palm, to show how the two stars

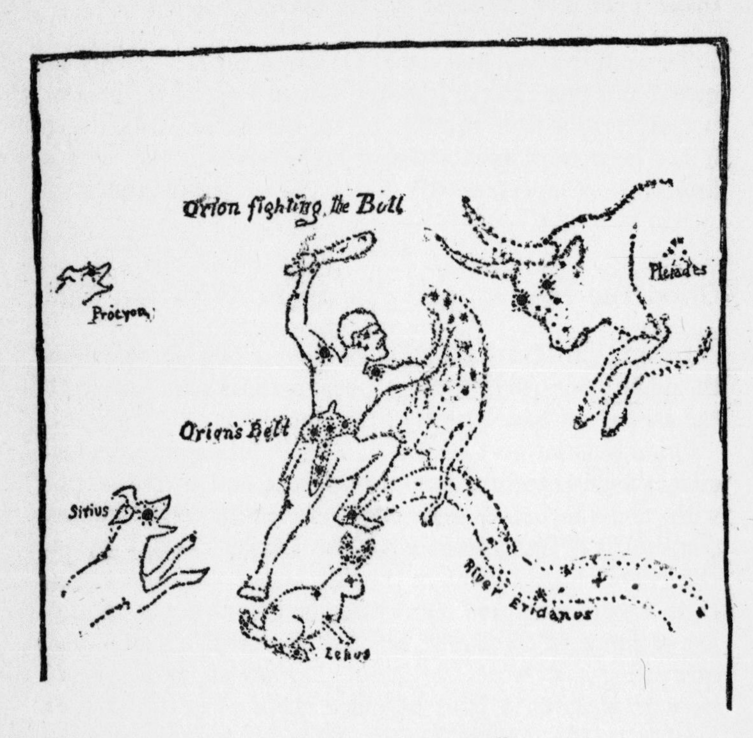

Orion Fighting the Bull

seem to him. When the mother is sure that he did see them clearly, she rejoices. She goes to the fire and drops a pinch of tobacco into it, for incense to carry her message, then looking toward the sky she says: "Great Spirit, I thank Thee that my child has the eyes of a hunter."

These things are not new, O Woodcrafter. The wise men of our race call the Big Star "Mizar" one of the chariot horses, and the little star "Alcor" or the Rider. In all ages it has been considered proof of first-class eyes, to see this little star. Can you see it? Have you the eyes of a hunter?

TALE 51

Orion the Hunter, and His Fight With the Bull

IN THE 49th Tale I told you there were two giants among the mighty hunters in the sky, Boötes, whose adventure with the Bears you have already heard, and Orion. (O-ry'-on).

Orion was the most famous of all. In his day men had no guns; they had nothing but clubs, spears, and arrows to fight with, and the beasts were very big and fierce as well as plentiful, yet Orion went whenever he was needed, armed chiefly with his club, fought the wild beasts, all alone, killing them or driving them out, and saving the people, for the joy of doing it. Once he killed a lion with his club, and ever afterward wore the lion's skin on his arm. Bears were as nothing to him; he killed them as easily as most hunters would rabbits, but he found his match, when he went after a ferocious wild Bull as big as a young elephant.

As soon as the Bull saw him, it came rushing at him. It happened to be on the other side of a stream, and as it plunged in, Orion drew his bow and fired seven quick shots at the Bull's heart. But the monster was coming head on, and the seven arrows all stuck in its shoulder, making it madder than ever. So Orion waved his lion skin in his left hand, and with his club in the right, ran to meet the Bull, as it was scrambling up the bank from the water.

The first whack of the club tumbled the Bull back into the water, but it turned aside, went to another place, and charged again. And again Orion landed a fearful blow with the club on the monster's curly forehead.

By this time, all the animals had gathered around to see the big fight, and the gods in heaven got so interested that they shouted out, "Hold on, that is good enough for us to see. Come up here."

So they moved the mighty Hunter and the Bull, and the River and all the animals, up to heaven, and the fight has gone on there ever since.

In the picture I have shown a lot of animals besides Orion and the Bull, but the only things I want you to look now in the sky, are Orion's belt with the three stars on it, and the Pleiades on the Bull's shoulder, the seven spots where the seven arrows struck.

And remember these stars cannot be seen in summer, they pass over us in winter time. You can find Orion by drawing a straight line across the rim of the Dipper, beginning at the inner or handle side, passing throught he outer or Pointers side, and continued for twice the length of the Dipper, handle and all, this will bring you to Betelgeuze, the big star in the Giant's right shoulder, below that are the three stars of his belt, sometimes called the "Three Kings."

TALE 52

The Pleiades, that Orion Fired at the Bull

WHEN late autumn comes the Pleiades (Ply'-a-dees) appear in the evening sky to the eastward. These are the seven shots in the Bull's shoulder, the seven arrows from

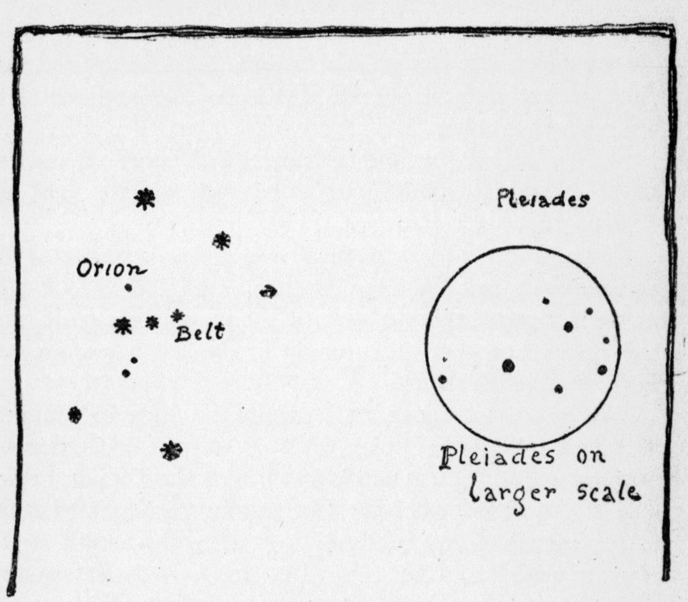

The Pleiades

Orion's bow. The Guide can locate them by continuing the line of Orion's belt, eight times the length of the belt to the right, as one faces the Hunter, so Orion must have been very close indeed. At first they look like a faint light with a few bright pin-points scattered through. Tennyson described them as:

> Glittering like a swarm of fireflies
> Tangled in a silver braid.

The best time to see them is some clear night about Christmas, when there is no moon, and the Pleiades are nearly overhead, above the mist and smoke of the horizon, and there are no electric lights near by.

Study them attentively. Make a tube of your two hands and look through. Look on the ground, then look back again; look not straight at them, but a little to one side; and at last, mark down on paper how many you can clearly see, putting a big spot for the big one, and little spots for the little ones. Poor eyes see nothing but a haze; fairly good eyes see four of the pin-points; good eyes see five; the best of eyes see seven. I can see seven on a clear winter night when there are no clouds and no moon. This is as high as you need expect to get, although it is said that some men in clear air on a mountain top have seen ten, while the telescope shows that there are 2,000.

In taking these eyesight tests you may use your spectacles if you usually wear them.

TALE 53

The Twin Stars

Two-Bright-Eyes went wandering out
To chase the Whippoorwill;
Two-Bright-Eyes got lost and left
Our teepee—oh, so still!

Two-Bright-Eyes was carried up
To sparkle in the skies
And look like stars—but we know well
That that's our lost Bright-Eyes.

She is looking for the camp,
She would come back if she could;
She still peeps thro' the tree-tops
For the teepee in the wood.

TALE 54

Stoutheart and His Black Cravat

Do you know the bird that wears a black cravat, which he changes once a year? It is the English Sparrow, the commonest of all our birds. His hair is gray, but he must have been redheaded once, for just back of his ears there is still a band of red; and his collar, maybe, was white once, but it is very dingy now. His shirt and vest are gray; his coat is brown with black streaks—a sort of sporting tweed. The new cravat comes when the new feathers grow in late summer; and, at first, it is barred with gray as if in half mourning for his sins. As the gray tips wear off, it becomes solid black; that is, in March or April. In summer, it gets rusty and worn out; so every year he puts on a new one in late August.

The hen sparrow is quite different and wears no cravat. She has a black-and-brown cape of the sporting pattern, but her dress is everywhere of brownish Quaker gray.

The song of the English Sparrow is loud and short; but he tries to make up, by singing it over and over again, for many minutes.

He eats many bad bugs, and would be well liked, if he

did not steal the nests and the food of Bluebirds, Woodpeckers, Swallows, and others that are prettier and more useful birds, as well as far better singers than he is.

But there is much to admire in the Sparrow. I do not know of any bird that is braver, or more ready to find a way out of trouble; and if he cannot find a way, he cheerfully makes the best of it.

Some years ago I was at Duluth during a bitterly cold spell of weather. The thermometer registered 20° or 30° below zero, and the blizzard wind was blowing. Oh my, it was cold. But out in the street were dozens of English Sparrows chirruping and feeding; thriving just as they do in warmer lands and in fine weather.

When black night came down, colder yet, I wondered what the little stout-hearts would do. Crawl into some hole or bird-house, maybe? or dive into a snowdrift? as many native birds do.

I found out; and the answer was most unexpected.

In front of the hotel was a long row of electric lights. At nine o'clock, when I chanced to open the window for a breath of air, my eye fell on these; on every bulb was an English Sparrow sound asleep with the overarching reflector to turn the storm, and the electric bulb below him to warm his toes. My hat is off. Our Department of Agriculture may declare war on the Sparrow; but what is the use? Don't you think that a creature who is not afraid of blizzard or darkness, and knows how to use electric lights, is going to win its life-battle, and that he surely is here to stay?

TALE 55

Tracks, and the Stories They Tell

SOMETIMES, in town, just after rain, when the gutters are wet, and the pavement dry, look for the tracks of some

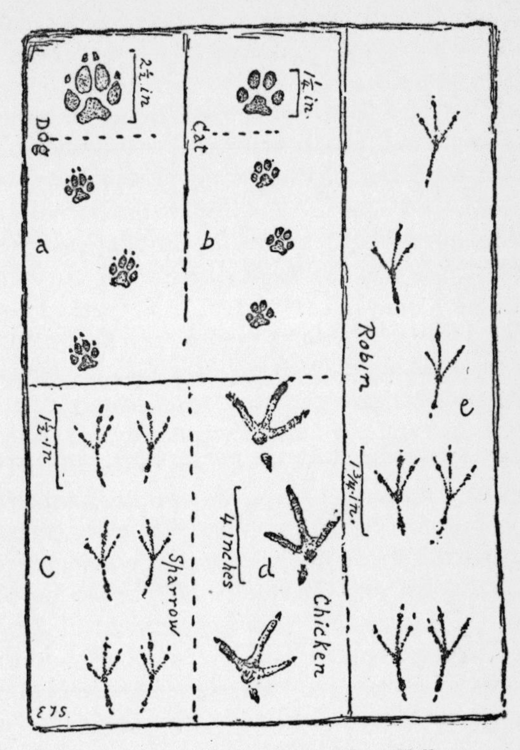

Tracks, and the Stories They Tell

Dog that walked with wet feet on the pavement. You will find that they are like "a" in the drawing. A Dog has five toes on his front feet, but only four touch the pavement as he walks. The claws also touch, and make each a little mark.

Now look for the track of a Cat; it is somewhat like that of the Dog, but it is smaller, softer, and the claws do not show (b). They are too good to be wasted on a pavement; she keeps them pulled in, so they are sharp when she has use for them.

Make a drawing of each of these, and make it life size.

When there is dust on the road, or snow, look for Sparrow tracks; they are like "c."

Note how close together the front three toes are. The inner two are really fast together, so they cannot be separated far and the hind toe is very large. Last of all, note that the tracks go two and two, because the Sparrow goes "hop hop, hop." These things mean that the Sparrow is really a tree bird; and you will see that, though often on the ground he gets up into a tree when he wishes to feel safe.

Look for some Chicken tracks in the dust; they are like "d" in the drawing because the Chicken does not go "hop, hop, hop" like the Sparrow, but "walk, walk, walk." The Chicken is a ground bird. Most of the song birds hop like the Sparrow, and most of the game birds walk like a Chicken. But the Robin (e) goes sometimes hopping and sometimes running, because part of his life is in the trees, and part on the ground.

TALE 56

A Rabbit's Story of His Life, Written by Himself

YES, the Rabbit wrote it himself and about himself in the oldest writing on earth, that is the tracks of his feet.

A WOODCRAFT TRAGEDY
As shown by the Tracks and Signs in the Snow

In February of 1885, one morning after a light snowfall, I went tramping through the woods north of Toronto, when I came on something that always makes me stop and look—the fresh tracks of an animal. This was the track of a Cottontail Rabbit and I followed its windings with thrills of interest. There it began under a little brush pile (a); the bed of brown leaves showing that he settled there, before the snow-fall began. Now here (b) he leaped out after the snow ceased, for the tracks are sharp, and sat looking around. See the two long marks of his hind feet and in front the two smaller prints of his front feet; behind is the mark made by his tail, showing that he was sitting on it.

Then he had taken alarm at something and dashed off at speed (c), for now his hind feet are tracking ahead of the front feet, as in most bounding forefoots, and the faster he goes, the farther ahead those hind feet get.

See now how he dodged about here and there, this way and that, among the trees, as though trying to escape some dreaded enemy (c, d, e, f).

But what enemy? There are no other tracks, and still the wild jumping went on.

I began to think that the Rabbit was crazy, flying from an imaginary foe; possibly that I was on the track of a March Hare. But at "g" I found on the trail for the first time a few drops of blood. That told me that the Rabbit was in real danger but gave no clue to its source.

At "h" I found more blood and at "j" I got a new thrill, for there, plain enough on each side of the Rabbit track, were finger-like marks, and the truth dawned on me that these were the prints of great wings. The Rabbit was fleeing from an eagle, a hawk, or an owl. Some twenty yards farther "k" I found in the snow the remains of the luckless Rabbit partly devoured. Then I knew that the eagle had not done it, for he would have taken the Rabbit's body away, not eaten him up there. So it must have been a hawk or an owl. I looked for something to tell me which, and I got it. Right by the Rabbit's remains was the large twin-toed track (l) that told me that an owl had been there, and that therefore he was the criminal. Had it been a hawk the mark would have been as shown in the left lower corner, three toes forward and one back, whereas the owl usually sets his foot with two toes forward and two backward, as in the sketch. This, then, I felt sure was the work of an owl. But which owl? There were two, maybe three kinds in that valley. I wished to know exactly and, looking for further evidence, I found on a sapling near by a big soft, downy, owlish feather (m) with three brown bars across it; which told me plainly that a Barred Owl or Hoot Owl had been there recently, and that he was almost certainly the killer of the Cottontail.

This may sound like a story of Sherlock Holmes among the animals—a flimsy tale of circumstantial evidence. But while I was making my notes, what should come flying through the woods but the Owl himself, back to make another meal, no doubt. He alighted on a branch just above my head, barely ten feet up, and there gave me the best of proof, next to eye witness of the deed, that all I had gathered from the tracks and signs in the snow was quite true.

I had no camera in those days, but had my sketch book, and as he sat, I made a drawing which hangs to-day among my pictures that are beyond price.

Here, then, is a chapter of wild life which no man saw, which man could not have seen, for the presence of a man would have prevented it. And yet we know it was true, for it was written by the Rabbit himself.

If you have the seeing eye, you will be able to read many

strange and thrilling happenings written for you thus in the snow, the mud, and even the sand and the dust.

TALE 57

The Singing Hawk

LISTEN, Guide and young folk, I want to add another bird to your list to-day; another secret of the woods to your learning.

I want you to know the Singing Hawk, Our nature writers nearly always make their hawks scream, but I want you to know a wonderful Hawk, right in your own woods, that really and truly sings, and loves to do it.

It is a long time ago since I first met him. I was going past a little ravine north of Toronto, on a bright warm midwinter day, when a loud call came ringing down the valley and the bird that made it, a large hawk, appeared, sailing and singing, *kee-o*, *kee-o*, *kee-o*, *kee-o*, *kee-o*, *kee-ye-o*, *ky-ye-o*, *ky-oodle*, *ky-oodle*, *kee-o*, *kee-o* and on; over and over again, in a wild-wood tone that thrilled me. He sailed with set wings to a near-by tree, and ceased not his stirring call; there was no answer from the woods, but there was a vibrant response in my heart. It moved me through and through. How could it do so much, when it was so simple? I did not know how to tell it in words, but I felt it in my boyish soul. It expressed all the wild-wood life and spirit, the joy of living, the happy brightness of the day, the thrill of the coming spring, the glory of flight; all, all it seemed to voice in its simple ringing, "*kee-o*, *kee-o*, *kee-o*, *kee-yi-o*"; never before had I seen a bird so evidently rejoicing in his flight; then singing, it sailed away from sight; but the song has lingered ever since in the blessed part of my memory. I often heard it afterward, and many times caught the Blue-jay in a feeble imitation of its trumpet note. I never forgot the exact timbre of that woodland call; so when at length, long after, I traced it to what is known in books as the "Red-shouldered Hawk," it was a little triumph and a little disappointment. The books made it all so commonplace. They say it has a loud call like "kee-o"; but they do not say that it has a bugle note that can stir your very soul if you love the wild things, and voices more than any other thing on wings the glory of flight, the blessedness of being alive.

To-day, as I write, is December 2, 1917; and this morning as I walked in my homeland, a sailing, splendid hawk came pouring out the old refrain, "*kee-yi-o, kee-yi-o, kee-oh.*" Oh, it was glorious! I felt little prickles in the roots of my hair as he went over; and I rejoiced above all things to realize that he sang just as well as, yes maybe a little better than that first one did, that I heard in the winter woods some forty years ago.

TALE 58

The Fingerboard Goldenrod

"OH, MOTHER CAREY! All-mother! Lover of us little plants as well as the big trees! Listen to us little slender Goldenrods.

"We want to be famous, Mother Carey, but our stems are so little and our gold is so small, that we cannot count in the great golden show of autumn, for that is the glory of our tall cousins. They do not need us, and they do not want us. Won't you give us a little job all our own, our very own, for we long to be doing something?"

Then Mother Carey smiled so softly and sweetly and said: "Little slender Goldenrods, I am going to give you

The Compass Goldenrod Pointing Toward the North

something to do that will win you great honour among all who understand. In the thick woods the moss on the trunk shows the north side; when the tree is alone and in the open, the north side is known by its few branches; but on the open prairie, there is no plant that stands up like a finger post to point the north for travellers, while the sun is hid."

"This, then do, little slender Goldenrods; face the noon sun, and as you stand, throw back your heads proudly, for you are in service now. Throw back your heads till your golden plumes are pointing backward to the north—so shall you have an honourable calling and travellers will be glad that I have made you a fingerboard on the plains."

So the slender Goldenrod and his brothers rejoiced and they stood up straight, facing the noon sun, and bent backward, throwing out their chests till their golden caps and plumes were pointed to the north.

And many a traveller, on cloudy days and dark nights, has been cheered by the sight of the Compass Goldenrod, pointing to the north and helping him to get home.

This does not mean that every one of them points to the north all the time. They do their best but there are always some a little wrong. Yet you can tell the direction at night or on dark days if you look at a bed of them that grew out in full sunlight.

"Yon is the north," they keep on singing, all summer long, and even when winter comes to kill the plant, and end its bloom, the brave little stalk stands up there, in snow to its waist, bravely pointing out the north, to those who have learned its secret. And not only in winter storms, but I have even found them still on guard after the battle, when the snow melted in springtime. Once when I was a boy, I found a whole bank of them by a fence, when

The Shadow on the Snow.

WOODCHUCK DAY: COLD WEATHER

"To be, or not to be"

the snow went off in April, and I wrote in their honour this verse:

Some of them bowed are, and broken
  And battered and lying low
But the few that are left stand like spearmen staunch
  Each pointing his pike at the foe.

TALE 59

Woodchuck Day, February Second

Sixth Secret of the Woods

It was Monapini that told Ruth Pilgrim, and Ruth Pilgrim told the little Pilgrims, and the little Pilgrims told the little Dutchmen, and the little Dutchmen told it to all the little Rumours, and the grandchild of one of these little Rumours told it to me, so you see I have it straight and on good authority, this Sixth Secret of the Woods.

The story runs that every year the wise Woodchuck retires to sleep in his cozy home off the subway that he made, when the leaves begin to fall, and he has heard the warning. Mother Carey has sung the death-song of the red leaves; sung in a soft voice that yet reaches the farthest hills:

"Gone are the summer birds.
Hide, hide, ye slow-foots.
Hide, for the blizzard comes."

And Mother Earth, who is Maka Ina, cries to her own: "Come, hide in my bosom, my little ones." And the wise Woodchuck waits not till the blizzard comes, but hides while he may make good housing, and sleeps for three long moons.

But ever on the second sun of the Hunger-moon (and this is the Sixth Secret) he rouses up and ventures forth. And if so be that the sun is in the sky, and the snow on the bosom of his Mother Earth, so that his shadow shall appear on it, he goeth back to sleep again for one and a half moons more —for six long weeks. But if the sky be dark with clouds and the earth all bared of snow so that no shadow shows, he says, "The blizzard time is over, there is food when the ground is bare," and ends his sleep.

This is the tale and this much I know is true: In the North, if he venture forth on Woodchuck Day, he sees both sun and snow, so sleeps again; in the South there is no snow that day, and he sleeps no more; and in the land between, he sleeps in a cold winter, and in an open winter rouses to live his life.

These things I have seen, and they fit with the story of Monapini, so you see the little Rumour told me true.

THINGS TO KNOW

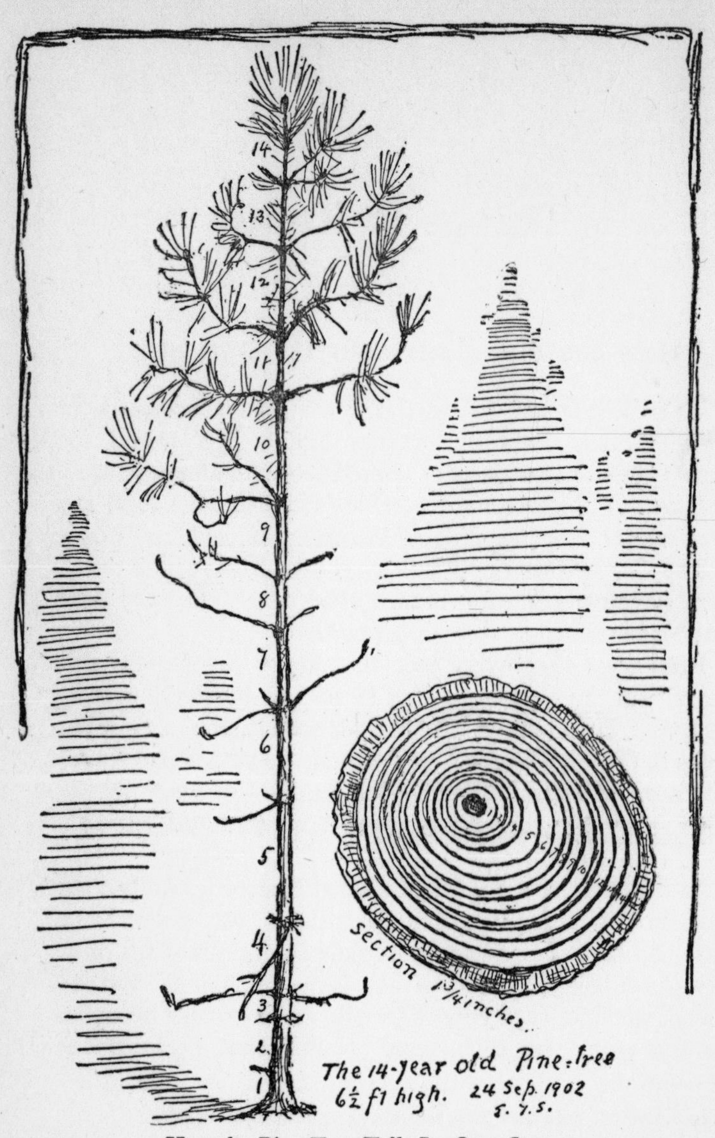

How the Pine Tree Tells Its Own Story

Things to Know

TALE 60

How the Pine Tree Tells Its Own Story

SUPPOSE you are in the woods, and your woods in Canada, or the Northern States; you would see at once two kinds of trees: Pines and Hardwoods.

Pines, or Evergreens, have leaves like needles, and are green all the year round; they bear cones and have soft wood.

The Hardwoods, or Broadleaves, sometimes called Shedders, have broad leaves that are shed in the fall; they bear nuts or berries and have hard wood.

Remember this, every tree that grows has flowers and seeds; and the tree can always be told by its seeds, that is, its fruit. If you find a tree with cones on it, you know it belongs to the Pine family. If you find one with broad leaves and nuts or berries, it belongs to the Hardwoods.*

Of these the Pines always seem to me more interesting.

In September, 1902, I had a good chance to study Pine trees in the mountains of Idaho. There was a small one that had to be cut down, so I made careful drawings of it. It was fourteen years old, and across the stump it showed one ring of wood for each year of growth, and a circle of branches on the trunk for each year. Notice that between the

*The Guide will note that there are rare exceptions to these rules.

branches, the trunk did *not* taper; it was an even cylinder, but got suddenly smaller at each knot by the same amount of wood as was needed by those branches for their wood.

If we begin in the centre of the stump, and at the bottom of the trunk, we find that the little tree tells us its own story of its life and troubles. Its first year, judging by the bottom section of the trunk (No. 1) and by the inmost ring, was just ordinary. Next year according to section 2 and ring 2, it had a fine season and grew nearly twice as much as the first year. The third year the baby Pine had a very hard time, and nearly died. Maybe it was a dry summer, so the little tree grew only 2½ inches higher while the ring of wood it added was no thicker than a sheet of paper. Next year, the fourth, it did better. And the next was about its best year, for it grew 7½ inches higher, and put on a fine fat ring of wood, as you see.

In its eleventh year, it had some new troubles; either the season was dry, or the trees about too shady, or maybe disease attacked it. For it grew but a poor shoot on the top, and the ring of wood on the stump is about the thinnest of all.

Of course, a saw-cut along the second joint showed but thirteen rings, and the third but twelve while one through the top joint, the one which grew this year, showed but a single ring.

Thus the Pine tree has in itself a record of its whole life; and this is easy to read when the tree is small; but in later life the lower limbs disappear, and the only complete record is in the rings of growth that show on the stump. These never fail to tell the truth.

Of course, you are not to go around cutting down trees merely to count their rings and read their history, but you should look at the rings whenever a new stump gives you a good chance. Then Hardwoods as well as Pines will spread before you the chapters of their life; one ring for each year that they have lived.

TALE 61

Blazes

ALL hunters and Indians have signs to let their people know the way. Some of these signs are on trees, and are called "Blazes." One of those much used is a little piece of bark chipped off to show the white wood; it means: "This is the way, or the place." Another sign is like an arrow, and means: "Over there," or "Go in that direction." No matter what language they speak, the blazes tell everyone alike. So a blaze is a simple mark that tells us something without using words or letters, and it depends on where it is placed for part of its meaning.

On the following page are some blazes used in our towns to-day. You will find many more if you look, some in books; some on the adjoining page.

TALE 62

Totems*

A TOTEM is a simple form used as the emblem or symbol of a man, a group of men, an animal, or an idea; it does not use or refer to words or letters, so it is the same in all languages. Unlike the blaze it does not depend on its position for part of its meaning.

Among peoples that cannot read or write, each leading man had a Totem that he used, instead of writing his name.

---

*The Guide will remember that Totemism and Tabuism were ideas which grew up long after the use of Totems began.

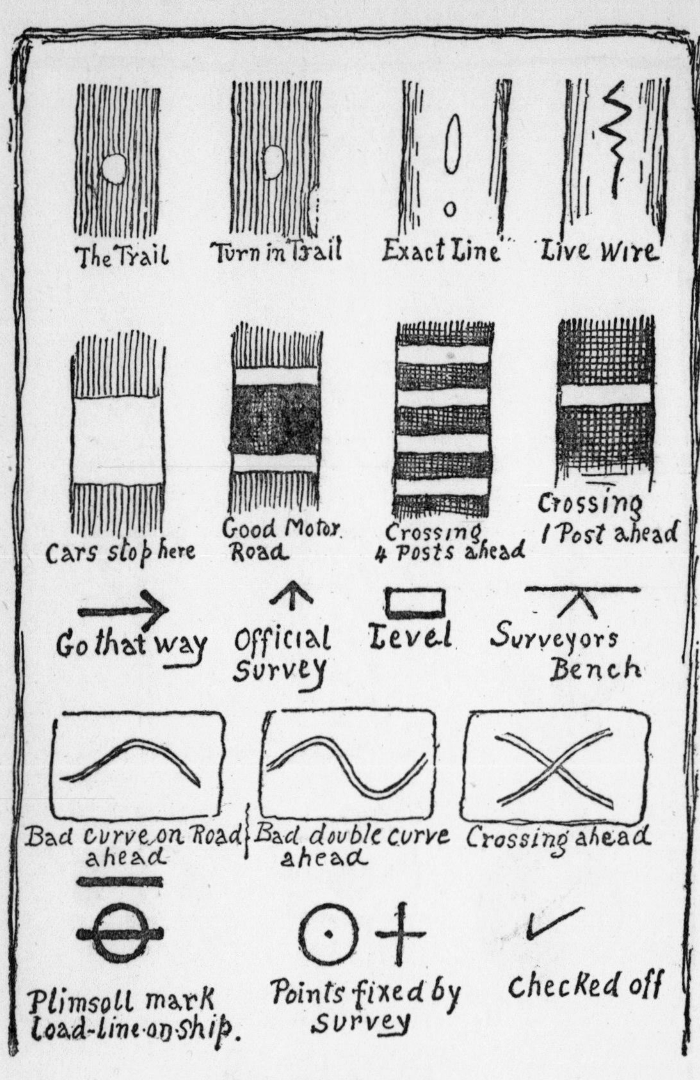
The Trail
Turn in Trail
Exact Line
Live Wire
Cars stop here
Good Motor Road
Crossing 4 Posts ahead
Crossing 1 Post ahead
Go that way
Official Survey
Level
Surveyors Bench
Bad curve on Road ahead
Bad double curve ahead
Crossing ahead
Plimsoll mark load-line on Ship.
Points fixed by Survey
Checked off

BLAZES.

Some well Known
TOTEMS

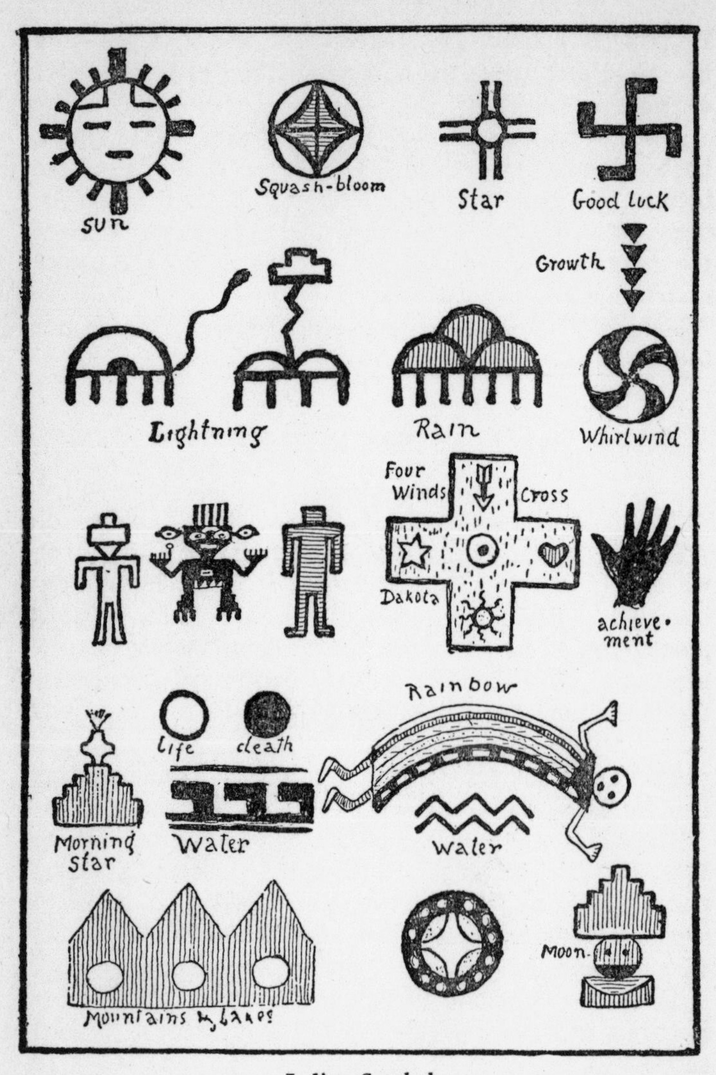

Indian Symbols

He put this mark on his property, and at length put it on his shield and armour to distinguish him in battle. Out of this grew heraldry.

Modern trade-marks are Totems though often spoiled by words or letters added. The Totem continues in use because it is so easy to see a long way off, and can be understood by all, no matter what their language. Most of the great railway companies have a Totem and the use of such things is increasing to-day.

Here in the drawing are some Totems seen daily in our towns. Doubtless you can add to the number.

TALE 63

Symbols

If you have thought much about it, O Guide! you will surely find that, for decoration, it is better to use a beautiful symbol of anything, rather than a good photograph of it. For the symbol lets the imagination loose, and the other chains it to the ground; the one is the spirit, and the other the corpse. These things you cannot tell to the little folks, but you can prove them to yourself, and you will see why I wish to give some symbols here for use.

There is another reason, one which you *can* give to them. It is this: Only the highly trained artist can make a good portrait drawing, while the smallest child, if it sticks to symbols, is sure, in some degree, of a pleasant success in its very first effort.

These that I give, are copied from Indian art, and whether in colour, in raised modelling, or in black lines, can be used successfully to decorate anything that you are likely to make.

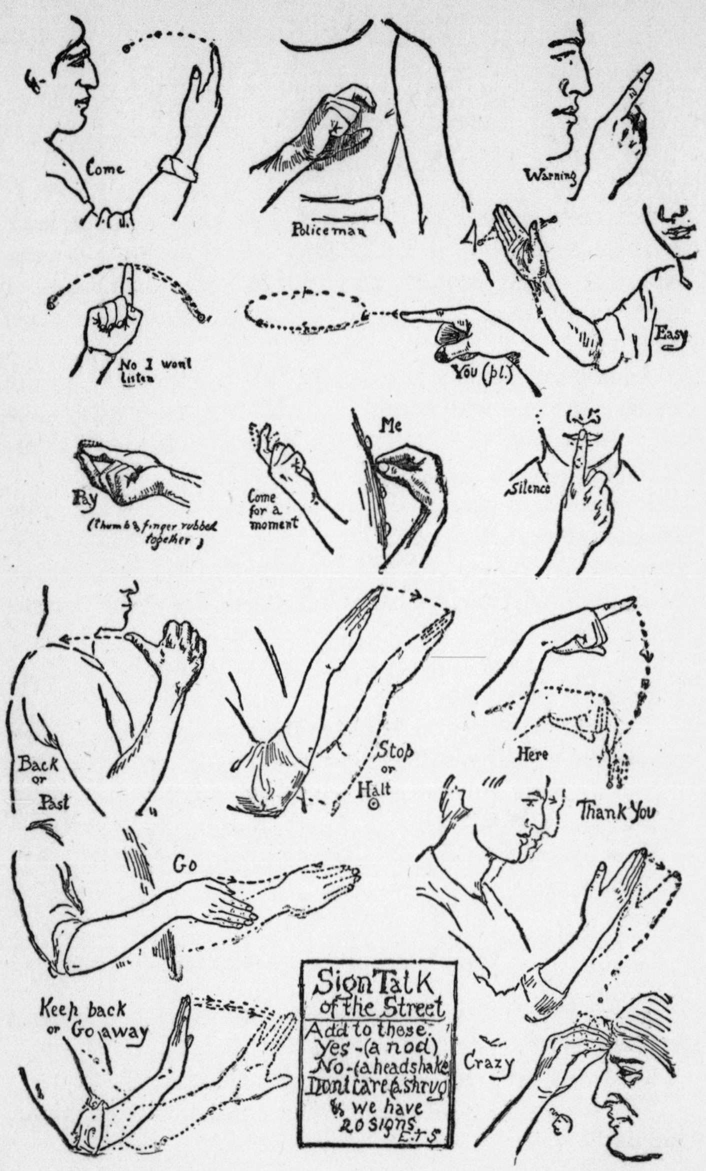

Seventeen Gestures Currently Used in the Sign Language

TALE 64

Sign Language

All men, especially wild men, and some animals have a language of signs. That is, they talk to each other without making any sounds; using instead, the movements of parts of the body. This is "eye talk," while words are "ear talk."

Among the animals, horses bob their heads when they are hungry and paw with a front foot when thirsty or eager to be off. Dogs wag their tails when pleased, and cows shake their heads when angry.

Policemen, firemen, railway men, and others use signs because there is too much noise to be heard. School children use signs because they are not allowed to talk in school. Most children know the signs for "yes" and "no," "come here," "go away," "hurry up," "you can't touch me," "hush!", "shame on you!", "up," "down," "word of honour," "swimming," etc.

The traffic policeman is using signs all day long. By a movement of the hand he signals:—stop, go on, come here, hurry up, wait, turn around, go by, stay back, over there, you look out, right here, and one or two others.

How many signs can you add to these two lists?

TALE 65

The Language of Hens

Yes; Hens talk somewhat as we do; only they haven't so many words, and don't depend on them as we have to.

There are only ten words in ordinary hen-talk.

The *cluck, cluck* of the mother means "Come along, kiddies."

The low *kawk* of warning, usually for a hawk.

The *chuck, chuck* of invitation means, "Good food."

The *tuk-ut-e-ah-tuk* means, "Bless my soul, what is that?"

The *cut, cut, get your hair cut,* of a Hen that has just laid and is feeling greatly relieved; no doubt, saying, "Thank goodness, that's done!" or maybe it is a notice to her mate or friend that "Business is over, let's have some fun. Where are you?"

The soft, long-drawn *tawk—tawk—tawk,* that is uttered as the Hen strolls about, corresponds to the whistling of the small boy; that is, it is a mere pastime, expressing freedom from fear or annoyance.

The long, harsh, *crauk, crauk* of fear when captured.

The quick *clack, clack, clatter* when springing up in fear of capture.

The *put, put* of hunger.

And, of course, the *peep, peep* of chickens and the *cock-a-doodle-doo,* which is the song of the Rooster.

Some Hens may have more; but these given here are hen-talk for mother-love, warning, invitation, surprise, exultation, cheerfulness, fear, astonishment, and hunger. Not a bad beginning in the way of language.

TALE 66

Why the Squirrel Wears a Bushy Tail

"Oh, Mother, look at that Gray Squirrel!" shouted Billie. "What a beautiful bushy tail he has!" Then, after a pause he added, "Mother, what is its tail for? Why is it so big and fluffy? I know a 'Possum has a tail to hang on a limb with, and a Fish can swim with his tail, but why is a Gray Squirrel's tail so bushy and soft?"

Alas! Mother didn't know, and couldn't tell where to

find out. It was long after, that little Billie got the answer to his childish, but really important question. The Alligator may use his tail as a club, the Horse, his tail as a fly-flapper, the Porcupine his tail as a spiked war-club, the 'Possum his as a hooked hanger, the Fox his as a muffler, the Fish his as a paddle; but the Gray Squirrel's tail is a parachute, a landeasy. I have seen a Gray Squirrel fall fifty feet to the ground, but his tail was in good condition; he spread it to the utmost and it landed him safely right side up.

I remember also a story of a Squirrel that lost his tail by an accident. It didn't seem to matter much for a while. The stump healed up, and the Squirrel was pert as ever; but one day he missed his hold in jumping, and fell to the ground. Ordinarily, that would have been a small matter; but without his tail he was jarred so severely that a dog, who saw him fall, ran up and killed him before he could recover and climb a tree.

TALE 67

Why a Dog Wags His Tail

THERE is an old story that the Dog said to the Cat: "Cat, you are a fool; you growl when you are pleased and wag your tail when you are angry." Which happens to be true; and makes us ask: Why does a Dog wag his tail to mean friendship?

The fact is, it is part of a wig-wag code, which is doubly interesting now that all our boys are learning wig-wagging with a white flag. We think that our army people invented this method; but Woodcraft men know better.

First, notice that any Dog that has any white on his body has at least a little white on the end of his tail. This is well known; and the reason is that the wild ancestor had a white brush on the end of his tail; a white flag, indeed; and this was the flag of his signal code.

Suppose, then, that a wild Dog, prowling through the woods, sights some other animal. Instantly he crouches; for it is good woodcraft to avoid being seen and then watch from your hiding-place. As the stranger comes near, the crouching Dog sees that it is one of his own kind, and that it is needless to hide any longer; indeed, that it is impossible to remain hidden. So the moment the stranger stops and looks at the crouching Dog, the latter stands straight up on all fours, raises his tail up high, and wags the white tip from side to side in the sign which means, "Let's be friends."

Every Dog knows the sign, every Dog in every town does it yet; every boy has seen it a thousand times. We flatter ourselves that we invented the wig-wag code with our little white flag. Maybe so; but the Dog had it long before we did.

TALE 68

Why the Dog Turns Around Three Times Before Lying Down

YES, they all do it; the big St. Bernard, the foolish littlest lap Dog, the ragged street Dog; give them bare boards, or a silken cushion, or snow, three turns around and down they go.

Why? Not so hard to answer as some simple questions. Long, long ago, the wild great-great-grandfather of the Dog—a yellow creature with black hair sprinkled on his back, sharp ears, light spots over his eyes, and a white tail-tip—used to live in the woods, or on the prairies. He did not have a home to which he might return every time he wanted to rest or sleep; so he camped wherever he found himself, on the plains, in a thicket, or even in some hole in a rock; and he carried his bedclothes on his back. But he always found it worth while to add a little comfort by smoothing the grass, the leaves, the twigs, or the pebbles before lying down; and the simplest way to do this was by curling up, and turning round three times, with the body brushing the high grass or pebbles into a comfortable shape for a bed.

Yes, and they all do it to-day just the same, big and little, which is only one of the many proofs that they are descended from the same wild-wood great-grandfather, and still remember his habits.

TALE 69

The Deathcup of Diablo

THE world went very well in those bright days of the long ago, when the wedding of El Sol and Maka Ina set all living things rejoicing. Green youth and sparkling happiness were everywhere. Only one there was—Diablo—who found in it poor comfort. He had no pleasure in the growing grass. The buttercups annoyed him with the gayness of their gold. It was at this time he chewed their stalks, so that many ever since have been flattened and mangled. And the cherry with its fragrant bloom he breathed on with his poison breath, so its limbs were burnt and blackened into horrid canker bumps. And poisonous froth he blew on the sprouting rose leaves, so they blackened and withered away. The jewel weed, friend of the humming birds, he trampled down, but it rose so many times and so bravely, that he left the yellow dodder like an herb-worm, or a root-born leech to suck its blood all summer long, and

The Deathcup Toadstool

break it down. Then to trail over the trunks of trees and suck their life, he left the demon vine, the Poison Ivy with its touch of burning fire. He put the Snapping Turtle in the beautiful lakes to destroy its harmless creatures and the Yellow-eyed Whizz he sent, and the Witherbloom with its breath of flame.

And last he made the Deathcup Toadstool, and sowed it in the woods.

He saw the Squirrels eating and storing up the sweet red russula. He saw it furnish food to mice and deer, so he fashioned the Deathcup Amanita to be like it; and scattered it wherever good mushrooms grew, a trap for the unwary.

Tall and shapely is the Deathcup; beautiful to look upon and smelling like a mushroom. But beware of it, a very little is enough, a morsel of the cup; the next night or maybe a day later the poison pangs set in. Too late perhaps for medicine to help, and Amanita, the Deathcup, the child of Diablo, has claimed another victim.

How shall we know the deadly Amanita among its kindly cousins, the good mushrooms? Wise men say by these:— The poison cup from which its springs; the white kid collar on its neck; the white or yellow gills; and the white spores that fall from its gills if the cup, without the stem, be laid gills down on a black paper for an hour.

By these things we may know the wan Demon of the woods, but the wisest Guides say to their tribe:—"Because death lurks in that shapely mushroom, though there are a hundred good for food, they are much alike, and safety bids you shun them; let them all alone."

So Diablo went on his way rejoicing because he had spoiled so much good food for good folk.

This, the danger of the Deathcup, is the Seventh Secret of the Woods.

The Poison Ivy

TALE 70

Poison Ivy or the Three-Fingered Demon of the Woods

You have been hearing about good fairies and good old Mother Carey and Medicine in the Sky. Now I am going to warn you against the three-fingered Demon, the wicked snakevine that basks on stone walls and climbs up the tree trunk, and does more harm than all the other plants, vines, trees, and bushes put together; for it is not like the Deathcup, easy to see and easy to let alone.

This is the Poison Ivy. Does it not look poisonous as it crawls snake-like up some trunk, sending suckers out into the tree to suck the sap; and oozing all over its limbs with poison in tiny wicked little drops? Sometimes it does not climb but crawls on the ground, but by this ye may always know it: It has only three fingers on its hand; that is, only three leaflets on each stalk.

The one thing that looks like it, is the Boston Ivy, but that does not grow in the woods, and the Poison Ivy leaf always has the little bump and bite out on the side of the leaf as you see in the drawing.

It is known and feared for its power to sting and blister the skin when it is handled or even touched. The sting begins with an unpleasant itching which gets worse, especially if rubbed, until it blisters and breaks open with sores which are very hard to heal.

The cause of the sting is a blistering oil, which is found in tiny drops on all parts of the leaf and branches; it is a fixed oil; that is, it will not dry up, and as long as it is on the skin, it keeps on burning and blistering, worse and worse.

THE CURE

And this is the cure for the sting of the Demon Vine:—

Anything that will dissolve and remove oil without injuring the skin:—

Hot water, as hot as you can stand it, is good; a little salt in it helps.

Hot soapy water is good.

Hot water with washing soda is good.

A wash of alcohol is good.

But best of all is a wash of strong alcohol in which is a little sugar of lead as an antiseptic.

The Guide should remember that three persons out of five are immune from Poison Ivy, while a few are so sensitive that they are poisoned by flies carrying it to them on their feet. It can be easily cured if treated at once; if neglected it often becomes very bad and may need the help of a doctor.

This is the Eighth Secret of the Woods.

TALE 71

The Medicine in the Sky

THIS is one of the greatest and best secrets of Woodcraft—The Medicine in the Sky.

Let me tell you a story about it. There was once an Indian who left his own people, to live with the white man, in the East. But the Great Spirit was displeased, for he did not mean the Indian to live in houses or cities. After a year, the red man came back very thin and sick, coughing nearly all night, instead of sleeping. He believed himself dying.

The wise old Medicine Man of his tribe said, "You need the Medicine of the Sky." He took it and got quite well and strong.

Another Indian, who had gone to visit with a distant tribe of red men, came back with some sickness on his skin that made it very sore. It was far worse than Poison Ivy, for it began to eat into his flesh. The Medicine Man said, "Sky Medicine will cure you." And it did.

One day a white man, a trader, came with chest protectors to sell to the Indians. He was sure they needed them, because he did; and, although so well wrapped up, he was always cold. He suffered whenever the wind blew. The old Medicine Man said, "We don't need your chest pads, and you would not if you took the Sky Medicine." So the trader tried it, and by and by, to his surprise and joy, no matter whether it was hot or cold outdoors, he was comfortable.

This man had a friend who was a learned professor in a college, and he told him about the great thing he had learned from the old Indian. The professor was not old, but he was very sick and feeble in body. He could not sleep nights. His hair was falling out, and his mind filled with gloomy thoughts. The whole world seemed dark to him. He knew it was a kind of disease, and he went away out West to see his friend. Then he met the Medicine Man and said to him, "Can you help me?"

The wise old Indian said, "Oh, white man, where do you spend your days?"

"I spend them at my desk, in my study, or in the classroom."

"Yes, and your nights?"

"In my study among my books."

"And where do you sleep?"

"I don't sleep much, though I have a comfortable bed."

"In the house?"

"Yes, of course."

"Listen, then, O foolish white man. The Great Spirit set Big Medicine in the sky to cure our ills. And you hide from it day and night. What do you expect but evil? This do and be saved. Take the Sky Medicine in measure of your strength."

He did so and it saved him. His strength came back. His cheeks grew ruddy, his hands grew steady, his hair ceased falling out, he slept like a baby. He was happy.

Now what is the Sky Medicine? It is the glorious sunlight, that cures so many human ills. We ask every Woodcrafter to hold on to its blessings.

And in this wise, O Guide, you must give it to the little ones. Make it an honourable exploit to be sunburnt to the elbows without blistering; another to be sunburnt to the shoulders; another to the waist; and greatest of all, when sunburnt all over. How are they to get this? Let them go to some quiet place for the last, and let the glory fall on their naked bodies, for ten minutes each day. Some more, and some less, according to their strength, and this is the measure—so long as it is pleasant, it is good.

In this way they will inherit one of the good things of the woods and be strong and hardened, for there is no greater medicine than the Sun in the sky.

TALE 72

The Angel of the Night

O Guide of the young Tribe! Know you the Twelfth Secret of the Woods? Know you what walked around your tent on that thirtieth night of your camp out? No!

I think you knew, if you continued for thirty nights, but you knew not that you knew. These things, then, you should have in heart, and give to those you are leading.

The Great Spirit does not put out good air in the daytime and poison air at night. It is the same pure air at night, only cooler. Therefore use more clothing while you sleep. But while the outdoor air is pure, the indoor may be foul. Therefore sleep out of doors, and you will learn the blessedness of the night, and the night air, with its cooling kindly influence laden.

Those who come here to our Camp from life in town and sleeping in close rooms, are unaccustomed, and nervous it may be, so that they sleep little at first. But each night brings its balm of rest. Strength comes. Some know it in a week. The town-worn and nerve-weary find it at farthest in half a moon. And in one full moon be sure of this, when the night comes down you will find the blessed balm that the Great Spirit meant for all of us. You will sleep, a calm sweet vitalizing sleep.

You will know this the twelfth secret of the woods: What walked around your tent that thirtieth night? You know not, you heard nothing, for you slept. Yet when the morning comes you feel and know that round your couch, with wings and hands upraised in blessed soothing influence, there passed the Angel of the Night, with healing under her wings, and peace. You saw her not, you heard her not, but the sweet healing of her presence will be with you for many after moons.

THINGS TO DO

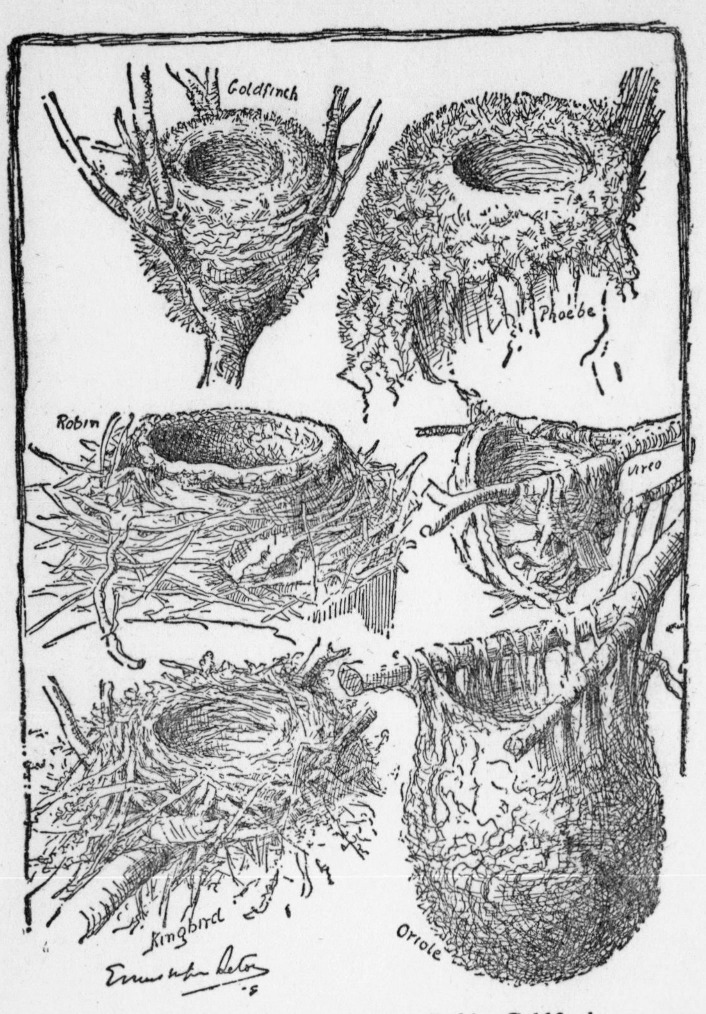

Nests of Kingbird, Oriole, Vireo, Robin, Goldfinch, Phoebe ($\frac{1}{4}$ life size)

Things to Do

TALE 73

Bird-nesting in Winter

WHAT good are old bird-nests? These are some of the ends they serve. A Deermouse seeking the safety of a bramble thicket and a warm house, will make his own nest in the forsaken home of a Cat-bird. A Gray Squirrel will roof over the open nest of a Crow or Hawk and so make it a castle in the air for himself. But one of the strangest uses is this: The Solitary Sandpiper is a bird that cannot build a tree nest for itself and yet loves to give to its eggs the safety of a high place; so it lays in the old nest of a Robin, or other tree bird, and there its young are hatched. But this is only in the Far North. There are plenty of old bird-nests left for other uses, and for you.

Bird-nesting in summer is wicked, cruel, and against the law. But bird-nesting in winter is good fun and harms no one, if we take only the little nests that are built in forked twigs, or on rock ledges. For most little birds prefer to make a new nest for themselves each season.

If you get: A Goldfinch, floss nest;
A Phoebe, moss nest;
A Robin, mud nest;
A Vireo, good nest;
A Kingbird, rag nest;
An Oriole, bag nest;
you have six different kinds of beautiful nests that are

The Ox-eye Daisy or Marguerite

easily kept for the museum, and you do no harm in taking them.

TALE 74

The Ox-eye Daisy or Marguerite

Do you know that "Daisy" means "day's eye," because the old country Daisy opens its eyes when day comes, and shuts them every night. But our Daisy is different and much bigger, so we have got into the way of calling it "Ox-eye." Some of our young people call it "Love-me; love-me-not," because they think it can tell if one is loved. They pull out the white rays of the flower one by one, saying, "He loves me; he loves me not; he loves me; he loves me not." Then what they are saying as the last is pulled, settles the question. If the Daisy says "He loves me," they take a second Daisy and ask the next question, "Will he marry me?" Then, pulling the rays as before, "This year, next year, some time, never." And in this way they learn all that the Daisies know about these important matters.

We call it "our Daisy," but it is not a true native of America. Its home is Europe. The settlers of New England, missing the flower of their homeland, brought it over and planted it in their gardens. It spread widely in the North; but it did not reach the South until the time of the Civil War, when it is said to have gone in with the hay for Sherman's Army, to become a troublesome weed in the fields.

This scrap of history is recorded in a popular ballad.

There's a story told in Georgia
  'Tis in everybody's mouth,
That 'twas old Tecumseh Sherman
  Brought the Daisy to the South.
Ne'er that little blossom stranger
  In our land was known to be,
Till he marched his blue-coat army
  From Atlanta to the sea.

The Monkeys in the Tree Tops

TALE 75

A Monkey-hunt

WE ALL love to go a-hunting; every one of us in some way; and it is only the dislike of cruelty and destruction that keeps most of us from hunting animals continually, as our forebears did.

Some of my best days were spent in hunting. The Arabs say, "Allah reckons not against a man's allotted span the days he spends in the chase."

I hope that I may help many of you to go a-hunting, and to get the good things of it, with the bad things left out.

Come! Now it is the spring of the year, and just the right time for a Monkey-hunt. We are going prowling along the brookside where we are pretty sure of finding our game. "See, there is a Monkey tree and it is full of the big Monkeys!"

"What! That pussy-willow?"

Yes, you think they are only pussy-willows, but wait until you see. We shall take home a band of the Monkeys, tree and all, and you will learn that a pussy-willow is only a baby Monkey half done.

Now let us get a branch of live elderberry and one or two limbs of the low red sumac. It is best to use sumac because it is the only handy wood that one can easily stick a pin through, or cut. The pieces should be five or six inches long and about half an inch to an inch thick. They should have as many odd features as possible, knots, bumps, fungus, moss, etc.; all of which add interest to the picture.

To these we must add a lot of odd bits of dry cane, dry grasses, old flower-stalks, moss, and gravel, etc., to use for background and foreground in the little jungle we are to make for our Monkeys to play in. It is delightful to find the new interest that all sorts of queer weeds take on, when we view them as canes or palms for our little jungle.

Now with the spoils of our hunt, let us go home and preserve the trophies.

Cut off about three inches of the elderberry wood and have it clear of knots; cut a flat ended ramrod so as just to fit the bore, and force out the pith with one clean sharp push: or else whittle away the surrounding wood. The latter way gives a better quality of pith.

Now take a piece of the pith about one-third the size of a big pussy-willow, use a very sharp knife and you will find it easy to whittle it into a Monkey's head about the shape of "a" and "b."

Use a very sharp-pointed, soft black pencil to make the eyes, nose, the line for the mouth and the shape of the ears; or else wait till the pith is *quite dry*, then use a fine pen with ink.

If you are skilful with the knife you may cut the ears so that they hang as in "d."

Stick an ordinary pin right down through the crown of the head into a big pussy-willow that will serve as a body (e). If you glue the head on it is harder to do, but it keeps the body from being mussed up. Cut two arms of the pith (ff) and two feet (gg), drawing the lines for the fingers and toes, with the sharp black pencil, or else ink as before.

Cut a long, straight pointed piece of pith for a tail, dip it in boiling water, then bend it to the right shape "h."

Cut a branch of the sumac so that it is about four inches high, and of the style for a tree; nail this on a block of wood to make it stand. Sometimes it is easier to bore a hole in the stand and wedge the branch into that.

Set the Monkey on the limb by driving the pin into it as at "i," or else glueing it on; and glue on the limbs and tail. Sometimes a little wad of willow-down on the Monkey's crown is a great help. It hides the pin.

Now set this away for the glue to harden.

Meanwhile take an ordinary cigar box about two inches deep, line it with white paper pasted in; or else paint it with water colour in Chinese white. Colour the upper part sky colour; the lower, shaded into green, getting very dark on the bottom. Lay a piece of glass or else a scrap of an old motor-car window-isinglass on the bottom, and set in a couple of tacks alongside to hold it; this is for a pool.

Make a mixture of liquid glue, one part; water, five parts; then stir in enough old plaster of Paris, whitening, or even fine loam to make a soft paste. Build banks of this paste around the pool and higher toward the back sides. Stick the tree, with its stand and its Monkeys, in this, to one side; dust powder or rotten wood over the ground to hide its whiteness; or paint it with water colours.

Use all the various dry grasses, etc., to form a jungle; sticking them in the paste, or glueing them on.

And your jungle with its Monkeys is complete.

Many other things may be used for Monkeys. I have seen good ones made of peanuts, with the features inked on, and a very young black birch catkin for tail. Beautiful birds also can be made by using a pith body and bright feathers or silks glued on for plumes. The pith itself is easily coloured with water colours.

You will be delighted to see what beautiful effects you can get by use of these simple wild materials, helped with a little imagination.

And the end of the Monkey-hunt will be that you have learned a new kind of hunting, with nothing but pleasant memories in it, and trophies to show for proof.

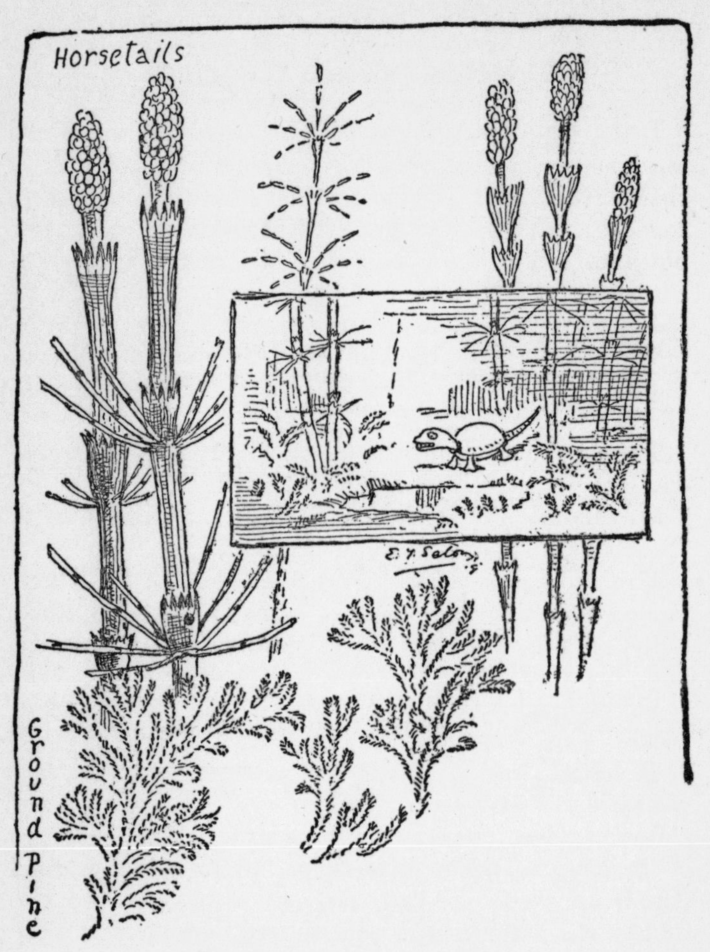

The Horsetail and the Jungle

TALE 76

The Horsetail and the Jungle

LONG, long ago, millions of years ago, this world was much hotter than it is now. Yes, in mid-winter it was hotter than it is now in mid-summer. Over all Pennsylvania there were huge forests of things that looked a little like palms, but some looked like pipes with joints, and had wheels of branches or limb wheels at every joint. They were as tall as some palms, and grew in swamps.

When one of those big joint-wheels fell over, it sank into the mud and was forgotten. So at last the swamp was filled up solid with their trunks.

Then for some unknown reason all the big joint-trees died, and the sand, mud, and gravel levelled off the swamp. There they lay, and slowly become blacker and harder under the mud, until they turned into coal.

That is what we burn to-day, the trunks of the wheel-jointed swamp trees. But their youngest great-grandchild is still with us, and shows, in its small way, what its great ancestors were like.

You will find it along some railway bank, or in any damp woods. Country people who know it, call it Joint Grass or Horsetails; the books call it Equisetum. The drawing will show you what to look for.

Gather a handful and take them home. Then get some of the moss known as ground-pine, a small piece of glass (the Guide should see that the edges of the glass are well rubbed with a stone, to prevent cutting the fingers), a cigar box, and white paste or putty, as in the Monkey-hunt.

Make a pool with the glass, and banks around it of the paste. Now cover these banks with the ground pine; using a little glue on the under side of each piece, but leave an open space without moss at the back, near the pool. Take a pointed stick and make holes through the moss into the clay or putty, and in each hole put one of the Horsetails, cutting it off with scissors if too tall for the top, till you have a thicket of these stems on each side; only make more on one side than on the other.

Now for the grand finish. You must make an extinct monster. Get half a walnut shell; cut a notch at one end where the neck will be; fill the shell with putty; stick in wooden pegs for legs, tail, and head. The central stalk of a tulip-tree fruit makes a wonderful sculptured tail; the unopened buds of dogwood do for legs, also cloves have been used. Any nobby stick serves for head if you make eyes and teeth on it.

When dry this makes a good extinct monster. Set it on the far bank of the water, and you have a jungle, the old Pennsylvania jungle of the days when the coal was packed away.

TALE 77

The Woods in Winter

Go out to the nearest chestnut tree, and get half a small burr; trim it neatly. Fill it with putty; set four wooden pegs in this for legs, a large peg for a head and a long thin one for a tail. On the head put two little black pins for eyes. Now rub glue on the wooden pegs and sprinkle them with powdered rotten wood, or fine sand, and you have a Burr Porcupine. Sometimes carpet tacks are used for legs. You will have to wear strong leather gloves in making this, it is so much like a real Porcupine.

Now go into your woods and get a handful of common red cedar twigs with leaves on, or other picturesque branches, some creeping moss of the kind used by flower dealers to pack plants, various dried grasses, and a few flat or sharp-cornered pebbles. Take these home. Get a cigar box or a candy-box, some paper, clay or putty and glass, as already described for the Monkey-hunt. Make a pond with the glass and a bank with the clay and pebbles. Paint the top of the clay, and tops of the pebbles with the thin glue, and also part of the glass; then sprinkle all with powdered chalk, whitening, plaster of Paris or talcum powder for snow. Put the Porcupine in the middle, and you have the "Woods in Winter."

TALE 78

The Fish and the Pond

Go out and get the cone of a Norway Spruce tree, or a White Spruce; this is the body of your Fish. Cut two round spots of white paper for eyes, glue them on, and when dry, put a black ink spot in the middle of each. Add a curved piece of paper on each side for gills. Then with an awl or with the point of the scissors make holes in the sides, in which put fins cut out of brown paper, fixing them in with glue. Then, with the knife blade, make a long cut in the back, and split the tail, and in each cut glue a thick piece of brown paper cut fin shape. When dry, draw lines on these with ink. Now you have a good Fish.

For the pond, take a cigar-box, paint the lower quarter of it dark green, and the upper part shaded into light blue, for sky. Glue a piece of glass or else carwindow celluloid level across this near the bottom. This is for water. Hide all the back and side edges of the glass with clay banks as described in the Monkey-hunt, or with moss glued on. Put a fine black thread to the Fish's back, another to his

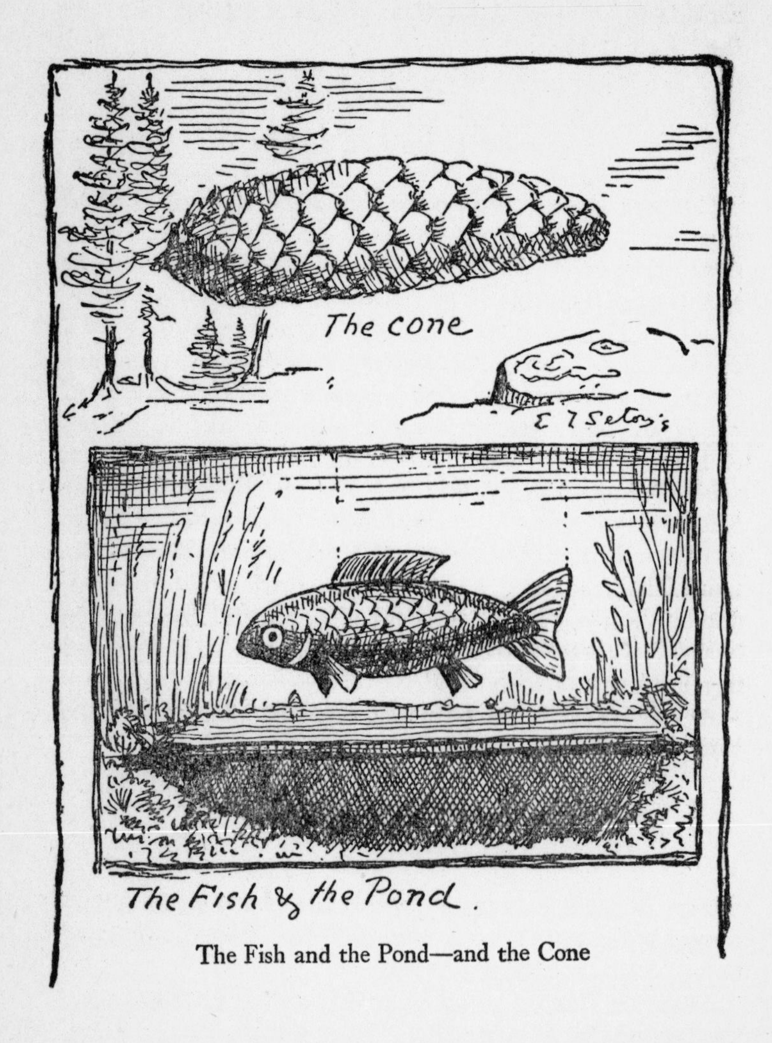

The Fish and the Pond—and the Cone

tail, and hang him level above the water by fastening the threads to the top of the box. Label it "Pond Life" or the "Fish at Home."

TALE 79

Smoke Prints of Leaves

COLLECT one or two leaves that have strongly marked ribs; elm and raspberry are good ones. Take a piece of paper that is strong, but rather soft, and about as big as this page. Grease, or oil it all over with paint-oil, butter, or lard. Then hold it, grease-side down, in the smoke of a candle, close to the flame, moving it about quickly so that the paper won't burn, until it is everywhere black with soot.

Lay the paper flat on a table, soot-side up, on a piece of blotting paper. Lay the leaf on this; then, over that, a sheet of paper. Press this down over all the leaf. Lift the leaf and lay it on a piece of soft, white paper; press it down as before, with a paper over it, on which you rub with one hand while the other keeps it from slipping; lift the leaf, and on the lower paper you will find a beautiful line-drawing of the leaf, done in black ink; which, once it is dry, will never rub out or fade away.

At one corner write down the date and the name of the leaf.

TALE 80

Bird-boxes

YOU can win honours in Woodcraft if you make a successful bird-box. That is one made by yourself, and used by some bird to raise its brood in.

There are three kinds of birds that are very ready to use the nesting places you make. These are the Robin, Wren,

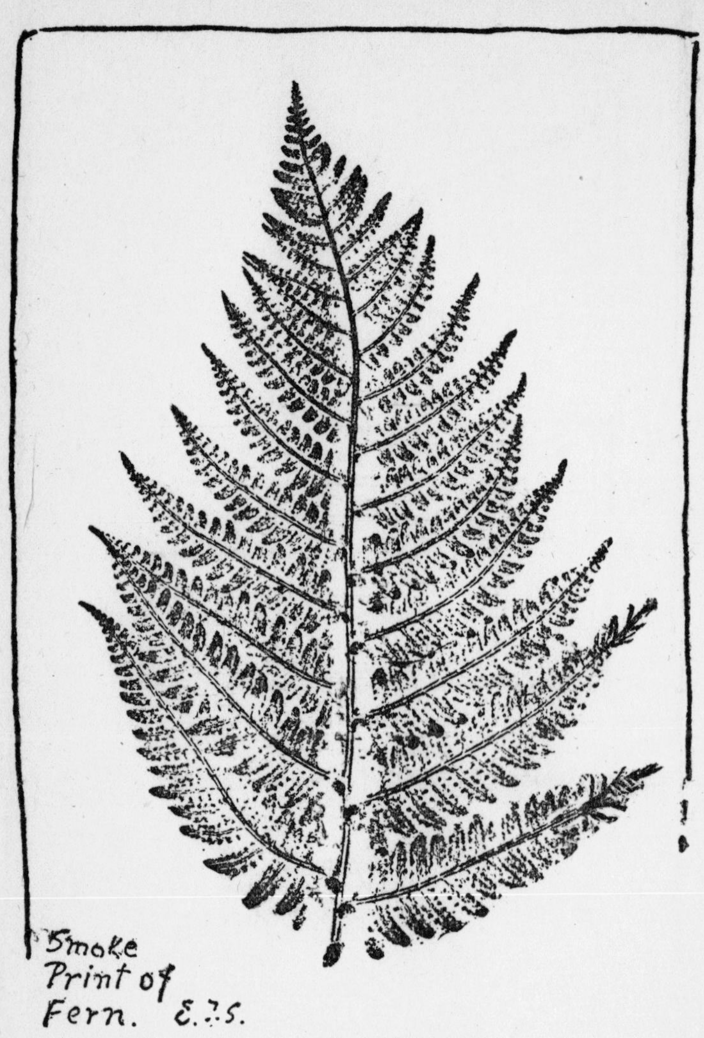

Smoke Prints of Leaves

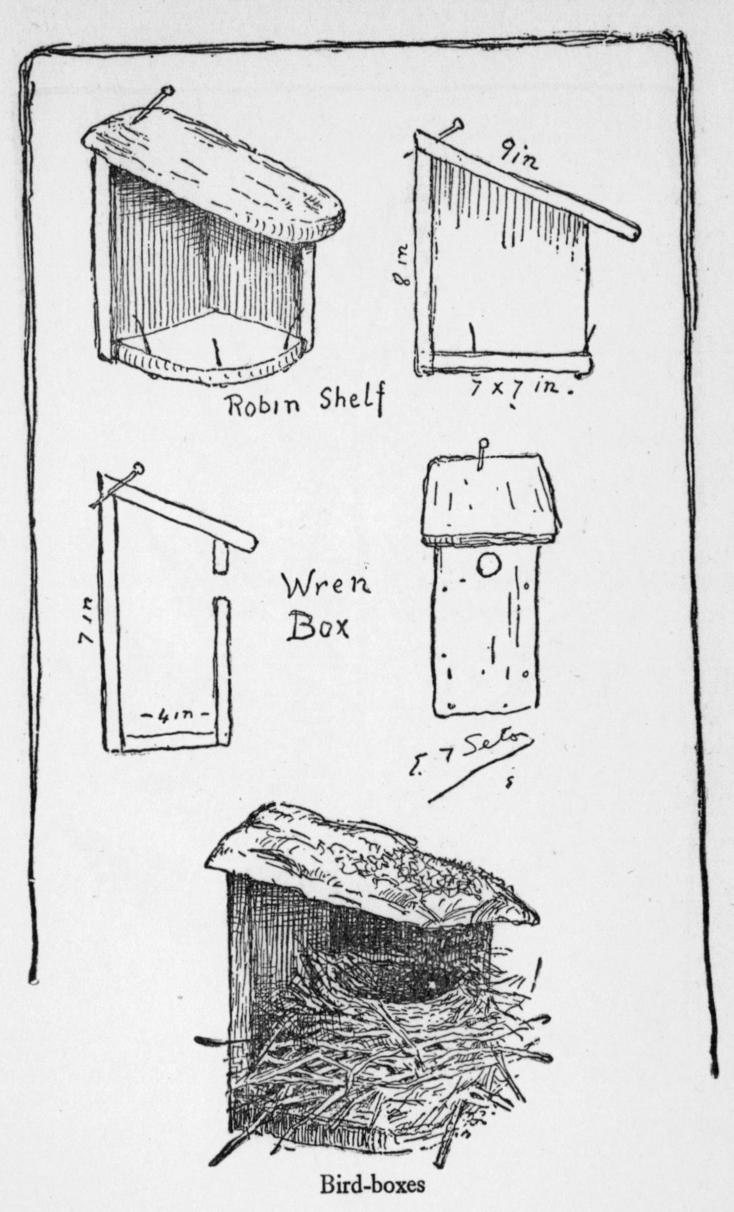

Bird-boxes

A Hunter's Lamp

and Phoebe. But each bird wants its own kind exactly right, or will not use it.

First the Robin wants a shelf, as in the picture. It should be hung against a tree or a building, about ten feet up, and not much exposed to the wind. It should also be in a shady place or at least not where it gets much sun.

The nails sticking up on the floor are to hold the nest so the wind will not blow it away. The Phoebe-shelf is much the same only smaller.

The Wren-box should be about four or five inches wide and six inches high inside, with a hole exactly seven eighths inch wide. If any bigger, the Wren does not like it so well, and other birds may drive the Wren away. Many Wren-boxes are made of tomato tins, but these are hard to cut a hole in. The Wren-box should be hung where the sun never shines on it all summer, as that would make it too hot inside.

TALE 81

A Hunter's Lamp

IN THE old pioneer days, every hunter used to make himself a lamp, for it was much easier to make than a candle. It is a good stunt in Woodcraft to make one. Each woodcrafter should have one of his own handiwork. There are four things needed in it: The bowl, the wick, the wick-holder and some fat, grease, or oil.

For the bowl a big clam shell does well.

For wick a strip of cotton rag rolled into a cord as thick as a slate pencil, and about two inches long; a cotton cord will do, or perhaps the fibrous bark of milkweed or other native stuff is the truly woodcraft thing.

For wick-holder get a piece of brick, stone, or a small clam shell about as big as a half dollar. Bore a hole through the middle to hold the wick. It is not easy to get the hole through without splitting the stone, but sometimes one can find a flat pebble already bored. Sometimes one can make a disc of clay with a hole in it, then burn this hard in a fierce fire, but the most primitive way is to rub the bump of a small clam shell on a flat stone till it is worn through.

For oil use the fat, grease, lard, or butter of any animal, if it is fresh, that is without salt in it.

Fill the bowl with the grease, soak the wick in grease and set it in the holder so that half an inch sticks up; the rest is in the grease. The holder rests on the bottom of the bowl.

Light the end that sticks up. It will burn with a clear, steady light till all the oil is used up.

To have made a lamp that will burn for half an hour is counted an "honour" in Woodcraft, and may win you a badge if you belong to a Woodcraft Tribe.

TALE 82

The Coon Hunt

TAKE a little bundle of white rags, or paper, as large as a walnut; call this the "Coon." While all the young folks hide their eyes or go out of the room, the Guide puts the Coon on some place, high or low, but in plain view; then, going away from it, shouts "Coon!"

Now the young scouts have to find that Coon, each looking about for himself. As soon as one sees it, he says nothing, but sits down. Each must find it for himself, then sit down silently, until all are down. Last down is the "booby"; first down is the winner; and the winner has the right to place the Coon the second time, if the Guide does not wish to do it.

This is often played indoors and sometimes a thimble is used for the Coon.

TALE 83

The Indian Pot

THIS is something everyone can make, no matter how young, and each, including the Guide, should make one.

Get a lump of good stiff clay; yellow is better than blue, only because it is a better colour when finished.

Work the clay up with water till soft, pick out all stones, lumps, and straws. Then roll it out like a pancake; use a knife to cut this into laces a foot long and about as thick as a pencil.

Dip your fingers in water, take one of these laces and coil it round and round as in "a," soldering it together with water rubbed on and into the joints. Keep on adding, shaping and rubbing, till you have a saucer about three inches across and a quarter of an inch thick. Put this away in some shady place to set, or harden a little; otherwise it would fall down of its own weight.

After about an hour, wet the rim, and build up on that round and round with laces as before, until you have turned the saucer into a cup, about four inches across, and, maybe three inches high. Set this away to stiffen. Then finish the shape, by adding more coils, and drawing it in a little. When this has stiffened, make a "slip" or cream of clay and water, rub this all over the pot inside and out; use your fingers and a knife to make it smooth and even. When this is done, use a sharp point, and draw on the pot any of the Indian designs show in the sketches, using lines and dots for the shading.

Now set the pot in some shady place to dry. High above the stove in the kitchen is a good place, so long as it is not too near the stove-pipe. After one day bring it nearer the heat. Then about the second day, put it in the oven.

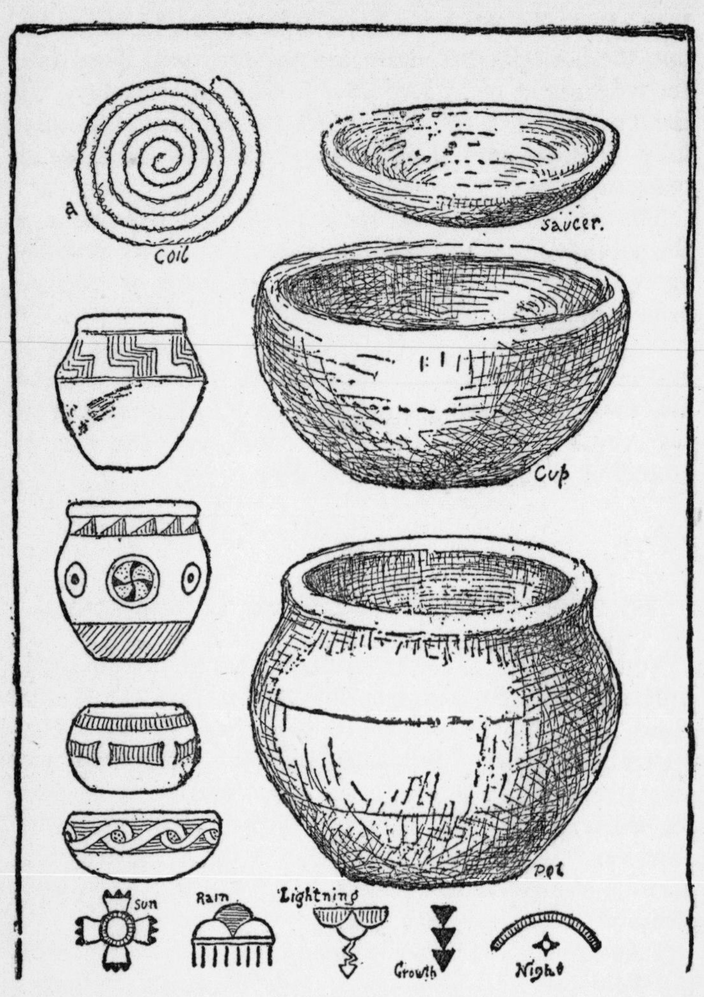

The Indian Pot

Last of all, and this is the hardest part to do, let the Guide put the bone-dry pot right into the fire, deep down into the red coals at night, and leave it there till next day. In the morning when the fire is dead, the pot should be carefully lifted out, and, if all is well, it will be of hard ringing red terra cotta.

The final firing is always the hardest thing to do, because the pots are so easily cracked. If they be drawn out of the fire while they are yet hot, the sudden touch of cold air usually breaks them into pieces.

Now remember, O Guide! A pot is made of the earth, and holds the things that come out of the earth to make life, that feed us and keep us. So on it, you should draw the symbols that stand for these things. At the foot of preceding page you see some of them.

TALE 84

Snowflakes, the Sixfold Gems of Snowroba

You have heard of the lovely Snowroba, white calm beautiful Snowroba, the daughter of King Jackfrost the Winter King, whose sad history was told in the first Tale. You remember how her robe was trimmed with white lace and crystal gems, each gem with six points and six facets and six angles, for that is one of the strange laws of the white Kingdom, the sixfold rule of gems. I did not give a good portrait of the White Princess, but I can show you how to make the Jewels which sparkled on her robe.

Take a square of thin white paper three or four inches wide (a). Fold it across (b), and again, until it is a square (c), half as wide as "a." Mark on it the lines as in "d," and fold it in three equal parts as in "e." Now with pencil draw the heavy black lines as in "f, g, h." Cut along these lines with scissors, open

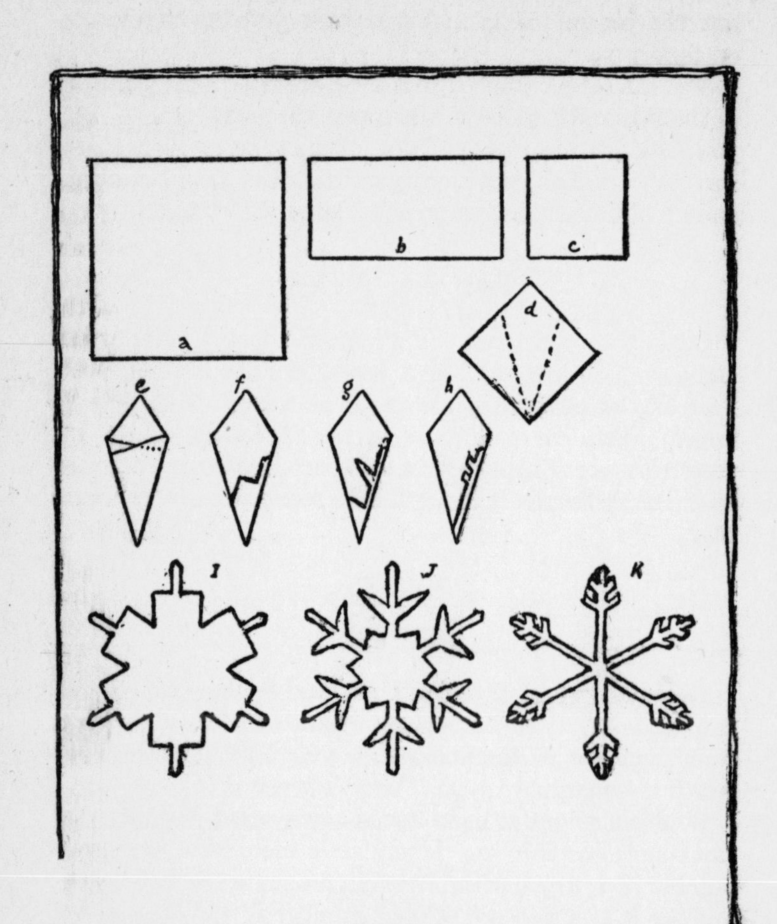

Snowflakes

out the central piece, and you have your snow-gems as on facing page.

You can see for yourself that these are true to the gem-law of the White Kingdom, if, when next the snow comes down, you look for the biggest flakes as they lie on some dark surface. You will find many patterns all of them beautiful, and all of them fashioned in accordance with the law.

Are You Alive?

Little boy or girl, are you all alive? Just as alive as an Indian? Can you see like a hawk, feel like a blind man, hear like an owl? Are you quick as a cat? You do not know! Well, let us find out in the next eight tales. In these tests 100 is kept in view as a perfect score in each department, although it is possible in some cases to go over that.

TALE 85

Farsight

1. HOLD up a page of this book, and see how far off you can read it. If at 60 inches, measured with a tapeline from your eye to the book, then your eye number is 60, which is remarkably good. Very few get as high as 70.

2. Now go out at night and see how many Pleiades you can count; see Tale 52. If you see a mere haze, your star number is 0; if you see 4 little pin points in the haze, your number is 8; if you see 6, your number is 12. If you see 7 your number is 14; and you will not get beyond that.

3. Now look for the Pappoose on the Squaw's back, as in Tale 50. If you do not see it, you score nothing. If you can see it, and prove that you see it, your number is 14 more.

Now add up these, thus: 60 plus 14 plus 14; this gives 88 as your *farsight* number. Anything over 60 means you can see like a hawk.

TALE 86

Quicksight

TAKE two boards, cards or papers, each about half a foot square; divide them with black lines into 25 squares each, i. e. 5 each way; get 6 nuts and 4 pebbles, or 6 pennies and 4 beans; or any other set of two things differing in size and shape.

Let the one to be tested turn his back, while the Guide places 3 nuts and 2 pebbles on one of the boards, in any pattern he pleases, except that there must be only one on a square.

Now, let the player see them for 5 seconds by the watch; then cover it up.

From memory, the player must place the other 3 nuts and 2 pebbles on the other board, in exactly the same pattern. Counting one for every one that was right. Note that a piece exactly on the line does not count; but one chiefly in a square is reckoned to be in that square.

Do this 4 times. Then multiply the total result by 5. This gives his *quicksight* number, to be added to his *aliveness* score.

TALE 87

Hearing

CAN you hear like an owl? An owl can find his prey by hearing after dark. His ears are wonderful. Let us try if yours are.

1. *Watch-test.* First, you must be blindfolded, and in some perfectly quiet place indoors. Now have the Guide hold a man's watch (open if hunting-cased), near your head; if you can hear it at 40 inches, measured on a tapeline, and prove that you do, by telling exactly where it is, in several tries, your hearing number is 40, which is high. If at 20 inches, it is low (20 pts.); if at 60 inches (60 pts.), it is remarkable. Anything over 50 points means you can hear like an owl. In this you go by your best ear.

2. *Pindrop-test.* Sometimes it is difficult to get a good watch-test. Then the trial may be made with an ordinary, silvered brass stick-pin, $1\frac{1}{8}$ inches long, with small head. Lay the pin on a block of wood that is exactly half an inch thick. Set this on a smooth polished board, or table top of hardwood, not more than an inch thick, and with open space under it. Set it away from the edge of the table so as to be clear of the frame and legs. After the warning "ready," let the Guide tip the block of wood, so the pin drops from the block to the table top (half an inch). If you hear it at 35 feet in a perfectly still room, your hearing is normal, and your hearing number is 35. If 20 feet is your farthest limit of hearing it, your number is 20, which is low. If you can hear it at 70 feet, your number is 70, which is remarkable.

You can use either the watch-test or the pin-test. If you use both, you add the totals together, and divide by 2, to get your *hearing* number.

TALE 88

Feeling

1. HAVE you got wise fingers like a blind man?

Put 10 nickels, 10 coppers and 10 dimes in a hat or in one

hand if you like. Then, while blindfolded, separate them into three separate piles, all of each kind in a separate pile, within 2 minutes. If it takes you the full 2 minutes (120 seconds), you are slow, and your feel number is 0. If you do it without a mistake in 1 minute and 20 seconds, your feel number is 40, one point for each second you are less than 2 minutes. But you must take off 3 points for every one wrongly placed, so 3 wrongly placed would reduce your 40 to 31. I have known some little boys on the East Side of New York to do it in 50 seconds without a mistake, so their feel-number by coins was 70. That is, 120 seconds minus 50 seconds equals 70. This is the best so far.

2. Now get a quart of corn or beans. Then when blindfolded, and using but one hand, lay out the corn or beans in "threes"; that is, three at a time laid on the table for 2 minutes. The Guide may move the piles aside as they are made. Then stop and count all that are exactly three in a pile (those with more or less do not count at all). If there are 40 piles with 3 in each, 40 is your number, by corn.

3. The last test is: Can you lace your shoes in the dark, or blind-folded, finishing with a neat double bow knot?

Arrange it so your two shoes together have a total of at least 20 holes or hooks to be used in the test, i. e., which do not have the lace in them when you begin. Allow 1 point for each hole or hook, i. e., 20 points, finish the lacing in 2 minutes, in any case stop when the 2 minutes is up; then take off 2 points for each one that is wrongly laced, or not laced. Thus: Supposing 4 are wrong, take off 4 times 2 from 20, and your blindfold lacing number is 12; if the number wrong was 10 or more, your lacing number is 0; if you had 3 wrong, your number is 14.

Suppose by these three tests—coins, corn, and laces—you

scored 40, 30, and 14; add these together and they give your *feel* number; 84.

TALE 89

Quickness

PUT down 12 potatoes (or other round things) in a row, each one exactly 6 feet from the last, and the last 12 feet from a box with a hole in it, just large enough to take in one potato. Now at the word "go," run and get the first potato, put it through the hole into the box; then get the second, bring it to the box, and so on, one at each trip. After one minute, stop. Now multiply the number of potatoes in the box by 10, and you have your *quickness* number. If you have 8 in the box, you score 80 points, you are as quick as a cat. Very few get over 80. No one so far has made 100 points.

TALE 90

Guessing Length

TAKE two common nails, or other thin bits of metal, and lay them on a table or board, at what you guess to be exactly one yard (36 inches) apart. Then let the Guide lay the tape-line on it, and, allowing 20 points for exactly right, take off 1 point for each half inch you are wrong, over or under. Do not count quarter inches, but go by the nearest half-inch mark. Do this 5 times, add up the totals, that will give your *guessing-length* number.

Thus, if your first guess turns out to be 37 inches, that is, 2 half-inches too much, 2 from 20 gives 18 points. Your next guess was 34 inches, that is 4 half-inches too little, 4 from 20 gives 16 points. Your next guess gave 12 points, your next 17, and your last 19. The total, 18 plus 16 plus 12 plus 17 plus 19, equals your number of *guessing length* or 82.

TALE 91

Aim or Limb-control

TAKE 25 medium-sized potatoes, and set up a bucket or bag whose mouth is round and exactly one foot across. Draw a line exactly 10 feet from the bucket or bag. Toe that line, and throw the potatoes, one by one, into the bag. Those that go in, then bounce out, are counted as in. Do it four times, then add up all the four totals of those that went in; that gives your *aim* or *control* number.

For example, suppose that in the 4 tries you got 10 in the first time, 15 in the second, 20 in the third, 19 in the fourth. Add these together, it gives your arm-control or *aim* number as 64.

Now add up all these high numbers:

Farsight	88
Quicksight	50
Hearing	50
Feeling	84
Quickness	80
Guessing Length	82
Aim	64
Your aliveness number is	498

But very few can score so high. If you can score 400 you are surely alive; you can see like a hawk, you can take in at a glance, you can hear like an owl, you can feel like a blind man, you are quick as a cat, you are a good judge of size, and you can aim true. That is, you are as *alive as an Indian*.

TALE 92

A Treasure Hunt

MAKE 24 little white sticks, each about three inches long, and as thick as a pencil. They are easy to make of willow shoots, after the bark is peeled off. While the young folk hide their eyes, the Guide walks off in the woods, ties a white rag on a tall stake or limb, for the point of beginning. Then, one step apart and in a very crooked line, sets each of the little white sticks in the ground, standing straight up. Under the last stick should be buried the treasure; usually a stick of chocolate. This the players are to find by following the sticks.

When the young folk get used to it, the line should be longer, the sticks farther apart, and the last one may be ten steps from the last but one.

When they are well trained at it, scraps of paper, white beans, corn, or even chalk marks on trees, instead of sticks, will serve for trail; and still later holes prodded in the ground with a sharp pointed cane will do.

This game can be played in the snow; in which case, the track of the Guide, when he hides the treasure, takes the place of the sticks.

Finally it makes a good game for indoors on a rainy day. In which case we use buttons, corn, or scraps of white cotton for trail sticks. Of course the trail now should be upstairs and down, and as long and crooked as possible.

TALE 93

Moving Pictures

ONE of the best developers of imagination is the Moving Picture. Sometimes called Pantomime, or Dumb-show which means all signs without sounds.

The one who is to put on the "movie" is given a subject and must then stand out on the stage or Council Ring, and carry all the story to the spectators, without using any sound and with as few accessories as possible.

The "print between the reels" is supplied by the Guide who simply announces what is needed to explain.

The following subjects have been used successfully (unless otherwise stated they are for one actor each):

Miss Muffet and the Spider—the well-known Nursery Rhyme

Old Mother Hubbard

Little Jack Horner

Mary and her Little Lamb

Red Ridinghood—walk through the woods, meeting the wolf, etc.

Robinson Crusoe—finding the track of a man in the sand

A Barber Shop—shaving a customer (two actors)

The Man's First Speech at a Dinner

The Politician who was rotten-egged after vainly trying to control a meeting

Joyride in a Ford Car—ending in a bad upset (two actors)

The Operation—a scene in a hospital following the accident (two or more)

The Professor of Hypnotism and His Subject (two actors)

The Man who Found a Hair in His Soup

The Young Lady Finds a Purse, on opening it a mouse jumps out and she remembers that it is 1st of April

A Young Man Telephoning to His Best Girl

A Man Meeting and Killing a Rattlesnake

Lighting a Lamp

Drawing a Cork

Looking for a Lost Coin—finding it in one pocket or shoe

A Musician Playing His Own Composition

The Sleeping Beauty and the Prince (two actors)

Goldilocks and the Three Bears

William Tell and the Apple (best rendered in caricature with a pumpkin and two actors)

Eliza Crossing the Ice

The Kaiser Signing His Abdication

The Judgment of Solomon (three actors)

Brutus Condemning His Two Sons to Death.

TALE 94

A Natural Autograph Album

If you live in the country, I can show you an old Woodcraft trick. Look for a hollow tree. Sometimes you can pick one out afar, by the dead top, and sometimes by noting a tree that had lost one of the biggest limbs years ago. In any case, basswoods, old oaks and chestnuts are apt to be hollow; while hickories and elms are seldom so, for once they yield to decay at all, they go down.

Remember that every hollow tree is a tenement house of the woods. It may be the home of a score of different families. Some of these, like Birds and Bats, are hard to observe, except at nesting time. But the fourfoots are easier to get at. For them, we will arrange a visitors' book at the foot of the tree, so that every little creature in fur will write his name, and some passing thought, as he comes to the tree.

How?

Oh, it is simple; I have often done it. First clear and level the ground around the tree for three or four feet; then cover it with a coat of dust, ashes, or sand—whichever is easiest to get; rake and brush it smooth; then wait over one night.

Next morning—most quadrupeds are night-walkers—

come back; and you will find that every creature on four feet that went to the tree tenement-house has left us its trail; that is its track or trace.

No two animals make the same trail, so that every Squirrel that climbed, every 'Coon or 'Possum, every Tree-mouse, and every Cottontail that went by, has clearly put himself on record without meaning to do so; and we who study Woodcraft can read the record, and tell just who passed by in the night.

TALE 95

The Crooked Stick

ONCE upon a time there was a girl who was very anxious to know what sort of a husband she should get; so, of course, she went to the old wood-witch.

The witch asked a few questions, then said to the girl: "You walk straight through that woods, turn neither to right nor left, and never turn back an inch, and pick me out a straight stick, the straighter the better; but pick only one, and bring it back."

So the girl set out. Soon she saw a fine-looking stick close at hand; but it had a slight blemish near one end, so she said: "No; I can do better than that." Then she saw another that was perfect but for a little curve in the middle, so she passed it by.

Thus she went, seeing many that were nearly perfect; but walking on, seeking one better, till she was quite through the woods. Then she realized her chances were nearly gone; so she had to take the only stick she could find, a very crooked one indeed, and brought it to the witch, saying that she "could have got a much better one had she been more easily satisfied at the beginning."

The witch took the stick, waved it at the girl and said:

"then this is your fortune; *through the woods and through the woods and out with a crooked stick.* If you were less hard to please, you would have better luck; but you will pass many a good man by, and come out with a crooked stick."

Maybe some of our Woodcraft girls can find an initiation in this. Put it just as the witch did it, but let it be considered a success if the stick is two feet long and nowhere half an inch out of true line. Let me add a Woodcraft proverb which should also have its mead of comfort—The Great Spirit can draw a straight line with a crooked stick.

TALE 96

The Animal Dance of Nana-bo-jou

For this we need a Nana-bo-jou; that is, a grown-up who can drum and sing. He has a drum and drumstick, and a straw or paper club; also two goblins, these are good-sized boys or girls wearing ugly masks, or at least black hoods with two eyeholes, made as hideous as possible; and any number of children, from three or four up, for animals. If each has the marks, colours, etc., of some bird or beast, so much the better.

First, Nana-bo-jou is seen chasing the children around the outside of the circle, trying to catch one to eat; but failing, thinks he'll try a trick and he says: "Stop, stop, my brothers. Why should we quarrel? Come, let's hold a council together and I will teach you a new dance."

The animals whisper together and the Coyote comes forward, barks, then says:

"Nana-bo-jou, I am the Coyote. The animals say that they will come to council if you will really make peace and play no tricks."

"Tricks!" says Nana-bo-jou, "I only want to teach you the new songs from the South."

Then all the animals troop in and sit in a circle. Nana-bo-jou takes his drum and begins to sing:

> "New songs from the South, my brothers,
> Dance to the new songs."

Turning to one, he says: "Who are you and what can you dance?"

The answers are, "I am the Beaver [or whatever it is] and I can dance the Beaver Dance."

"Good! Come and show me how."

So the Beaver dances to the music, slapping the back of his flat right hand, up and under his left hand for a tail, holding up a stick in both paws to gnaw it, and lumbering along in time to the music, at the same time imitating the Beaver's waddle.

Nana-bo-jou shouts: "Fine! That is the best Beaver Dance I ever saw. You are wonderful; all you need to be perfect is wings. Wouldn't you like to have wings so you could fly over the tree-tops, like the Eagle?"

"Yes," says the Beaver.

"I can make strong medicine and give you wings, if all the animals will help me," says Nana-bo-jou. "Will you?"

"Yes," they all cry.

"Then all close your eyes tight and cover them with your paws. Don't look until I tell you. Beaver, close your eyes and dance very fast and I will make magic to give you wings."

All close and cover their eyes. Nana-bo-jou sings very loudly and, rushing on the Beaver, hits him on the head with the straw club. The Beaver falls dead. The two goblins run in from one side and drag off the body.

Then Nana-bo-jou shouts: "Look, look, now! See how he flies away! See, there goes the Beaver over the tree-tops." All look as he points and seem to see the Beaver going.

Different animals and birds are brought out to dance their dances and are killed as before. Then the Crow comes out, hopping, flopping, cawing. Nana-bo-jou looks at him and says: "You are too thin. You are no good. You don't need any more wings," and so sends him to sit down.

Then the Coyote comes out to do the Coyote Dance, imitating Coyote, etc.; but he is very suspicious and, in answer to the questions, says: "No; I don't want wings. The Great Spirit gave me good legs, so I am satisfied"; then goes back to his seat.

Next the Deer, the Sheep, etc., come out and are killed; while all the rest are persuaded that the victims flew away. But the Coyote and the Loon have their doubts. They danced in their turns, but said they didn't want any change. They are satisfied as the Great Spirit made them. They are slow about hiding their eyes. At last, they peek and realize that it is all a trap and the Loon shouts: "Nana-bo-jou is killing us! It is all a trick! Fly for your lives!"

As they all run away, Nana-bo-jou pursues the Loon, hitting him behind with the club, which is the reason that the Loon has no tail and has been lame behind ever since.

The Loon shouts the Loon battle-cry, a high-pitched quavering LUL-L-L-O-O-O and faces Nana-bo-jou; the animals rally around the Loon and the Coyote to attack the magician. All point their fingers at him shouting "Wakan Seecha" (or Black Magic). He falls dead in the circle. They bury him with branches, leaves, or a blanket, and all the animals do their dances around him.

Before beginning, the story of the dance should be told to the audience.

TALE 97

The Caribou Dance

THE easiest of our campfire dances to learn, and the best for quick presentation, is the Caribou Dance. It has been put on for public performance after twenty minutes' rehearsing, with those who never saw it before, because it is all controlled and called off by the Chief. It does equally well for indoor gymnasium or for campfire in the woods.

In the way of fixings for this, you need only four pairs of horns and four cheap bows. Real deer horns may be used, but they are scarce and heavy. It is better to go out where you can get a few crooked limbs of oak, cedar, hickory or apple tree; and cut eight pairs, as near like those in the cut as possible, each about two feet long and one inch thick at the butt. Peel these, for they should be white; round off all sharp points of the branches, then lash them in pairs, as shown. A pair, of course, is needed for each Caribou. These are held in the hand and above the head, or in the hand resting on the head.

The four Caribou look best in white. Three or four hunters are needed. They should have bows, but no arrows. The Chief should have a drum and be able to sing the Muje Mukesin, or other Indian dance tune. One or two persons who can howl like Wolves should be sent off to one side, and another that can yell like a Lynx or a Panther on the other side, well away from the ring. Otherwise the Chief or leader can do the imitations. Now we are ready for

THE DANCE OF THE WHITE CARIBOU

The Chief begins by giving three thumps on his drum to call attention; then says in a loud, singing voice: "The

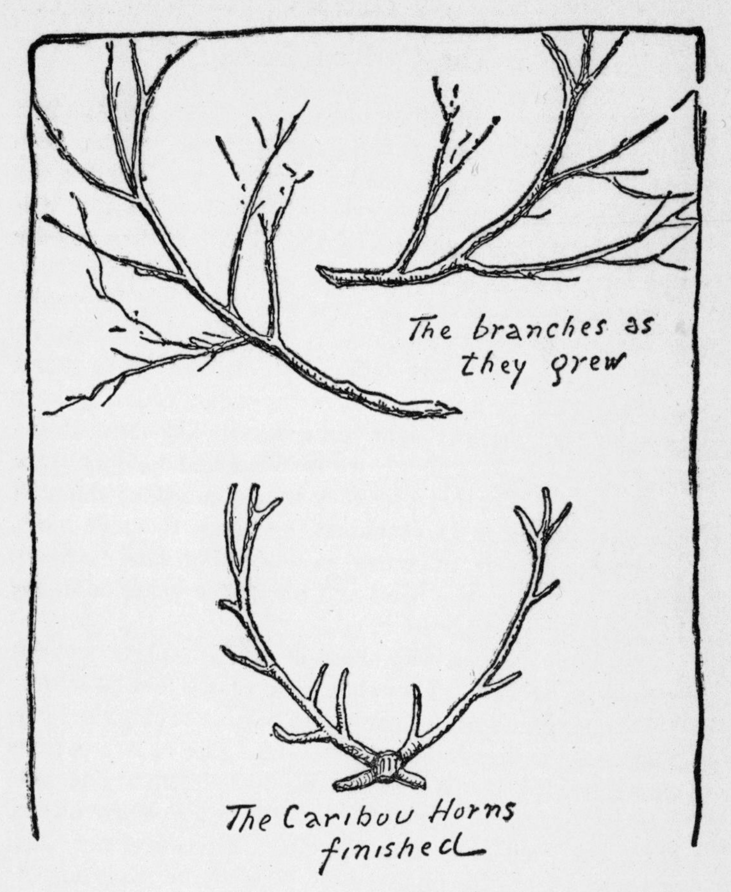

Horns for the Caribou Dance

Caribou have not come on our hunting grounds for three snows. We need meat. Thus only can we bring them back, by the big medicine of the Caribou Dance, by the power of the White Caribou."

He rolls his drum, then in turn faces each of the winds, beckoning, remonstrating, and calling them by name; Kitchi-nodin (West); Keeway-din (North); Wabani-nodin (East); Shawani-nodin (South). Calling last to the quarter whence the Caribou are to come, finishing the call with a long KO-KEE-NA. Then as he thumps a slow single beat the four Caribou come in in single file, at a stately pace timed to the drum. Their heads are high, and they hold the horns on their heads, with one hand, as they proudly march around. The Chief shouts: "The Caribou, The Caribou!" After going round once in a sun circle (same way as the sun), they go each to a corner. The Chief says: "They honour the symbol of the Great Spirit." The drum stops; all four march to the fire. They bow to it together, heads low, and utter a long bellow.

Then the Chief shouts: "They honour the four Winds, the Messengers."

Then the Caribou back up four paces each, turn suddenly and make a short bow, with a short bellow, then turn and again face the fire.

The Chief shouts: "Now they live their wild free lives on the plain." He begins any good dance song and beats double time. The Caribou dance around once in a circle.

The Chief shouts: "Full of life they fight among themselves."

The first and second Caribou, and third and fourth, close in combat. They lower their heads, lock horns held safely away from the head, snort, kick up the dust, and dance around each other two or three times.

The music begins again, and they cease fighting and dance in a circle once more.

The music stops. The Chief shouts: "They fight again." Now the first and fourth and second and third lock horns and fight.

After a round or so the music begins again and they cease fighting and again circle, dancing as before.

The Chief calls out: "The Wolves are on their track."

Now the howling of Wolves is heard in the distance, from the fellows already posted.

The Caribou rush toward that side and face it in a row, threatening, with horns low, as they snort, stamp, and kick up the dust.

The Wolf-howling ceases. The Caribou are victorious. The Chief shouts: "They have driven off the Wolves." They turn away and circle once to the music, holding their heads high.

Now Panther-yelling (or other menacing sound) is heard in the other direction. The Chief shouts: "But now the Panthers have found them out."

Again the Caribou line up and show fight. When it ceases, the Chief cries out: "They have driven off the Panther." Now they dance proudly around, heads up, chests out as they step, for they have conquered every foe.

Then the Chief calls out: "But another, a deadlier enemy comes. The hunters are on their trail." The hunters appear, crawling very low and carrying bows. They go half around the ring, each telling those behind by signs, "Here they are; we have found them," "Four big fellows," "Come on," etc. When they come opposite the Caribou, the first hunter lets off a short "yelp." The Caribou spring to the opposite side of the ring, and then line up to defy this new noise; but do not understand it, so gaze as they prance about in fear. The hunters draw their bows together, and make as though each lets fly an arrow. The first Caribou drops, the others turn in fear and run around about half of the ring, heads low, and not dancing; then they dash for the timber. The hunters run forward with yells. The leader holds up the horns. All dance and yell around the fallen Caribou and then drag it off the scene.

The Chief then says: "Behold, it never fails; the Caribou dance brings the Caribou. It is great medicine. Now there is meat in the lodge and the children cry no longer."

TALE 98

The Council Robe

THE Woodcraft Council Robe is something which every one may have, and should make for himself. It may be of any shade, of gray, buff, orange, or scarlet. The best ones are of a bright buff. In size they are about five feet by six feet, and the stuff may be wool, cotton, silk, or a mixture. My own is of soft or blanket cotton.

The robe is used as a wall banner, a personal robe, or a bed spread, and has for the first purpose two or more tag-loops sewn on the top. For the second, it has a head-hole or poncho-hole, an upright slit near one end (hh), and for the last, there are one or two buttons or tie-strings to close the poncho-hole. These are the useful features of the robe.

The ornamental features are the records on it. While these vary with each owner, the following usually appear: The Fourfold fire, near the middle; the Woodcraft shield, the owner's totem, the symbols of each coup and each degree won by the owner.

To this many add a pictographic record of great events or of camps they have visited.

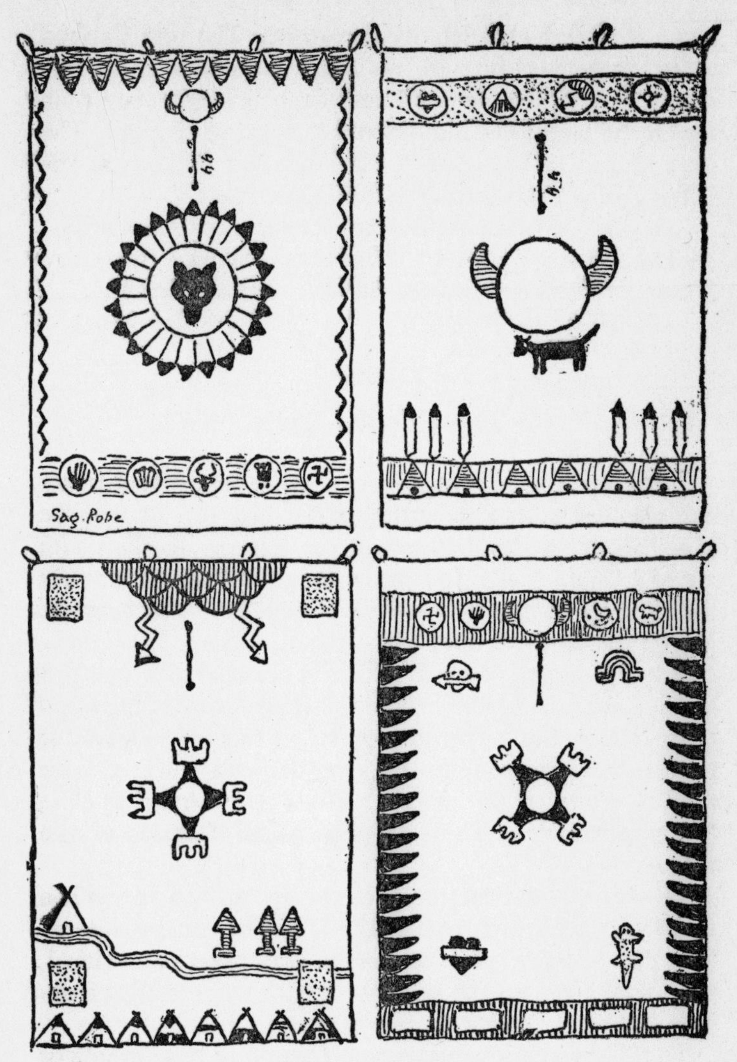

The Council Robe

The easiest way to make the robe is to use paints on the cotton fabric.

The favourite way and more beautiful way, is to use appliqués of coloured cloths for the design.

The most beautiful is to embroider in silk or mercerized cotton. But the last is very slow, and calls for much labour as well as some money.

On the preceding page are shown four different styles of robe; you may choose or adapt which you please, except that only a Sagamore may use the one with the 24 feathers in the centre.

THINGS TO REMEMBER

Things to Remember

TALE 99

How the Wren Became King of the Birds

THE story is very old, and it may not be true, but this is how they tell it in many countries.

The animals had chosen the lion for their King because his looks and his powers seemed to fit him best of all for the place. So the birds made up their minds that they also would have a royal leader.

After a long council it was decided that, in spite of strong opposition from the Ostrich and his followers, the one with the greatest powers of flight should be King. And away all flew to see which could go the highest.

One by one they came down tired out, till only two were to be seen in the air: the Eagle and the Turkey-buzzard still going up. At last they got so high that the Turkey-buzzard froze his ears off for they were naked. Then he gave it up. The Eagle went still higher to show how strong he was, then sailed downward to claim the royal honours.

But just as they were about to give him the crown, the Wren hopped off the top of the Eagle's head, where he had been hiding in the long feathers, and squeaked out, "No matter how high he was, I was a little bit higher, so I am King."

"You," said the Eagle; "Why I carried you up."

"Nothing to do with it," said the Wren.

"Then let's try it over," said the Eagle.

"No, no," said the Wren, "one try was agreed on, and it's settled now, I was higher than you."

And they have been disputing over it ever since. The lawyers take the Wren's side and the soldiers take the Eagle's side.

The peasants in Europe sometimes speak of the Eagle as "the King of the Birds," but they always call the Wren the "Little King." And that is why we call our gold-crowned Wrens, Kinglets, or Kingwrens and I suppose that is why they wear a crown of gold.

TALE 100

The Snowstorm

It was at the great winter Carnival of Montreal not long ago. Looking out of a window on a stormy day were five children of different races: an Eskimo, a Dane, a Russian, an Indian, and a Yankee. The managers of the Carnival had brought the first four with their parents; but the Yankee was the son of a rich visitor.

"Look," cried the little Eskimo from Alaska, as he pointed to the driving snow. "Look at the ivory chips falling! El Sol is surely carving a big Walrus tusk into a fine dagger for himself. See how he whittles, and sends the white dust flying."

Of course he didn't say "El Sol," but used the Eskimo name for him.

Then the Dane said: "No, that isn't what makes it. That is Mother Earth getting ready for sleep. Those are the goose feathers of her feather bed, shaken up by her servants before she lies down and is covered with her white mantle."

The little Indian, with his eyes fixed on the storm, shook

his head gravely and said: "My father taught me that these are the ashes from Nana-bo-jou's pipe; he has finished his smoke and is wrapping his blanket about him to rest. And my father always spake true."

"Nay, you are all wrong," said the little Russian. "My grandmother told me that it is Mother Carey. She is out riding in her strongest, freshest steed, the White Wind. He has not been out all summer; he is full of strength and fury; he spumes and rages. The air is filled with the foam from his bridle, and froth from his shoulders, as she rides him, and spurs him, and rides him. I love to see it, and know that she is filling the air with strength and with messages. They carry me back to my own dear homeland. It thrills me with joy to see the whiteness."

But the Yankee boy said: "Why, it's just snowing."

TALE 101

The Fairy Lamps

There was once a little barelegged, brown-limbed boy who spent all his time in the woods. He loved the woods and all that was in them. He used to look, not at the flowers, but deep down into them, and not at the singing bird, but into its eyes, to its little heart; and so he got an insight better than most others, and he quite gave up collecting birds' eggs.

But the woods were full of mysteries. He used to hear little bursts of song, and when he came to the place he could find no bird there. Noises and movements would just escape him. In the woods he saw strange tracks, and one day, at length, he saw a wonderful bird making these very tracks. He had never seen the bird before, and would have thought it a great rarity had he not seen its tracks everywhere. So he learned that the woods were full of beautiful creatures that were skillful and quick to avoid him.

One day, as he passed by a spot for the hundredth time, he found a bird's nest. It must have been there for long, and yet he had not seen it; and so he learned how blind he was, and he exclaimed: "Oh, if only I could see, then I might understand these things! If only I knew! If I could see but for once, how many there are, and how near! If only every bird would wear over its nest this evening a little lamp to show me!"

The sun was down now; but all at once there was a soft light on the path, and in the middle of it the brown boy saw a Little Brown Lady in a long robe, and in her hand a rod.

She smiled pleasantly and said: "Little boy, I am the Fairy of this Woods. I have been watching you for long. I like you. You seem to be different from other boys. Your request shall be granted."

Then she faded away. But at once the whole landscape twinkled over with wonderful little lamps—long lamps, short lamps, red, blue, and green, high and low, doubles, singles, and groups; wherever he looked were lamps—twinkle, twinkle, twinkle, here and everywhere, until the forest shone like the starry sky. He ran to the nearest, yes, a nest; and here and there, each different kind of lamp stood for another kind of nest. A beautiful purple blaze in a low tangle caught his eye. He ran to it, and found a nest he had never seen before. It was full of purple eggs, and there was the rare bird he had seen but once. It was chanting the weird song he had often heard, but never traced. But the eggs were the marvelous things. His old egg-collecting instinct broke out. He reached forth to clutch the wonderful prize, and—in an instant all the lights went out. There was nothing but the black woods about him. Then on the pathway shone again the soft light. It grew brighter, till in the middle of it he saw the Little Brown Lady—the Fairy of the Woods. But she was not smiling now. Her face was stern and sad, as she said: "I fear I set you over-high. I thought you better than the rest. Keep this in mind:

> "Who reverence not the
> lamp of life can never
> see its light."

Then she faded from his view, and he never saw the lamps again.

TALE 102

The Sweetest Sad Song in the Woods

ONCE a great American poet was asked which he thought was the sweetest voice in the woods. He said: "The sweetest sound in Nature is the calling of the Screech Owl."

Sometimes, though rarely, it does screech, but the sound it most often makes is the soft mournful song that it sings in the woods at night, especially in the autumn nights.

It seems to be moaning a lament for the falling leaves, a sad good-bye to the dear dying summer.

Last autumn one sat above my head in the dark October woods, and put his little soul into a song that seemed to be

> Ohhhh! Ohhhh!
> The leaves are falling:
> Ohhhh! Ohhhh!
> A sad voice calling;
> Ohhhh! Ohhhh!
> The Woodbirds flying;
> Ohhhh! Ohhhh!
> Sweet summer's dying,
> Dying, Dying.

The Lament of the Owl.

notation by Ann Seton

d.i.¼ = downward inflection ending a ¼ note lower than it began.
v.i.¼ = upward inflection etc.

A mist came into my eyes as I listened, and yet I thanked him. "Dear voice in the trees, you have said the things I felt, and could not say; but voicing my sadness you have given it wings to fly away."

TALE 103

Springtime, or the Wedding of Maka Ina and El Sol

OH, THAT was a stirring, glowing time! All the air, and the underwood seemed throbbed with pleasant murmuring voices. The streams were laughing, the deep pools smiling, as pussywillows scattered catkins on them from above. The oak trees and the birches put on little glad-hangers, like pennants on a gala ship. The pine trees set up their green candles, one on every big tip-twig. The dandelions made haste to glint the early fields with gold. The song toads and the peepers sang in volleys; the blackbirds wheeled their myriad cohorts in the air, a guard of honour in review. The woodwale drummed. The redbud draped its naked limbs in early festal bloom; and Rumour the pretty liar smiled and spread the news.

All life was smiling with the frank unselfish smile, that tells of pleasure in another's joy.

The love of love is wider than the world. And one who did not know their speech could yet have read in their reflected joy a magnitude of joyful happening, could guess that over two beings of the highest rank, the highest rank of happiness impended.

Yes, all the living world stood still at gaze: the story of the bridegroom, the gracious beauty of the bride were sung, for the wedding day had come. And Mother Carey, she was there, for were they not her peers? And the Evil One —he came, but slunk away, for the blessing of the one Great Oversoul was on them.

Oh, virile, radiant one, El Sol! Oh, Maka Ina! bounteous mother earth, the day of joining hand in hand passed by. The joy is with us yet; renewed each year, when March is three weeks gone. Look, then, ye wanderers in the woods! Seek in the skies, seek in the growing green, but find it mostly in your souls, and *sing!*

TALE 104

Running the Council

EVERY good Woodcrafter should know the way of the Council Ring.

Select some quiet level place out of doors; in the woods if possible, for it is so much better if surrounded by trees.

Make a circle of low seats; the circle should be not less than 12 feet or more than 20 feet across, depending somewhat on the number to take part.

In the middle prepare for a small fire. At one side is a special seat for the Chief; this is called the Council Rock.

On very important occasions take white sand or lime, and draw a circle around the fire. Then from that draw the four lamps and the twelve laws as in Tale 105.

When all is ready with the Guide on the Council Rock, and the Scouts in their seats, the Guide stands up and says: "Give ear my friends, we are about to hold a council. I appoint such a one, Keeper of the fire and so-and-so, Keeper of the tally. Now let the Fire-keeper light the fire."

Next the Tally-keeper calls the roll. After which the business part of the Council is carried on exactly the same as any ordinary meeting, except that instead of addressing the "Chairman," they say, "O Chief"; instead of "yes" they say "ho," instead of "no" they say "wah."

The order of doings in Council is:—

Opening and fire-lighting
Roll Call
Reading and accepting tally of last Council
Reports of Scouts (things observed or done)
Left-over business
New business
Honours
Honourable mention
(For the good of the Tribe) Complaints and suggestions.

(Here business ends and entertainment begins.)

Challenges
Games, contests, etc.
Close by singing Omaha Prayer (Tale 108)

TALE 105

The Sandpainting of the Fire

WHEN I was staying among the Navaho Indians, I met John Wetherall, the trader. He had spent half his life among them, and knew more of their ways than any other white man that I met. He told me that part of the education of Navaho priest was knowing the fifty sandpaintings of his tribe. A sandpainting is a design made on the ground or floor with dry sands of different colours—black, white, gray, yellow, red, etc. It looks like a rug or a blanket on the ground, and is made up of many curious marks which stand for some man, place, thing, or idea. Thus, the first sandpainting is a map of the world as the Navaho knew it, with rivers and hills that are important in their history. These sandpaintings cannot be moved; a careless touch spoils them, and a gust of wind can wipe them out. They

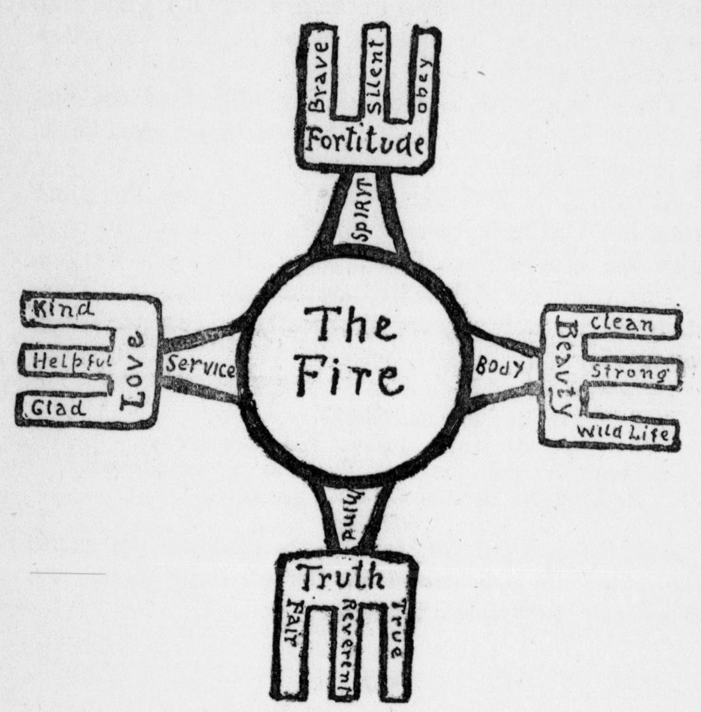

The Sandpainting of the Fire

endure only in the hearts and memories of the people who love them.

In the Woodcraft Camp there is but one sandpainting that is much used; that is, the Sandpainting of the Fourfold Fire. When I make it in camp, I use only white sand or powdered lime; but indoors, or on paper, I use yellow (or orange) and white.

This is the story of the sandpainting. The fire is the symbol of the Great Spirit; around that we draw a great circle, as in the diagram.

At each of the four sides we light another fire; these four are called Fortitude, Beauty, Truth, and Love, and come from the Fire through Spirit, Body, Mind, and Service.

Then from each of these we draw three golden rays. These stand for the twelve laws of Woodcraft, and they are named in this way:

> Be Brave, Be Silent and Obey;
> Be Clean, Be Strong, Protect Wild Life alway;
> Speak True, Be Reverent, Play Fair as you Strive!
> Be Kind; Be Helpful; Glad you are alive.

And the final painting is as in the drawing. Of course the names are not written on the real thing though the Woodcraft scout should know them.

TALE 106

The Woodcraft Kalendar

THE Woodcraft Kalendar is founded on the Indian way of noting the months. Our own ancestors called them "Moons" much as the Indians did. Our word "month" was once written "moneth" or "monath" which meant a "moon or moon's time of lasting." The usual names for the moons to-day are Latin, but we find we get closer to nature

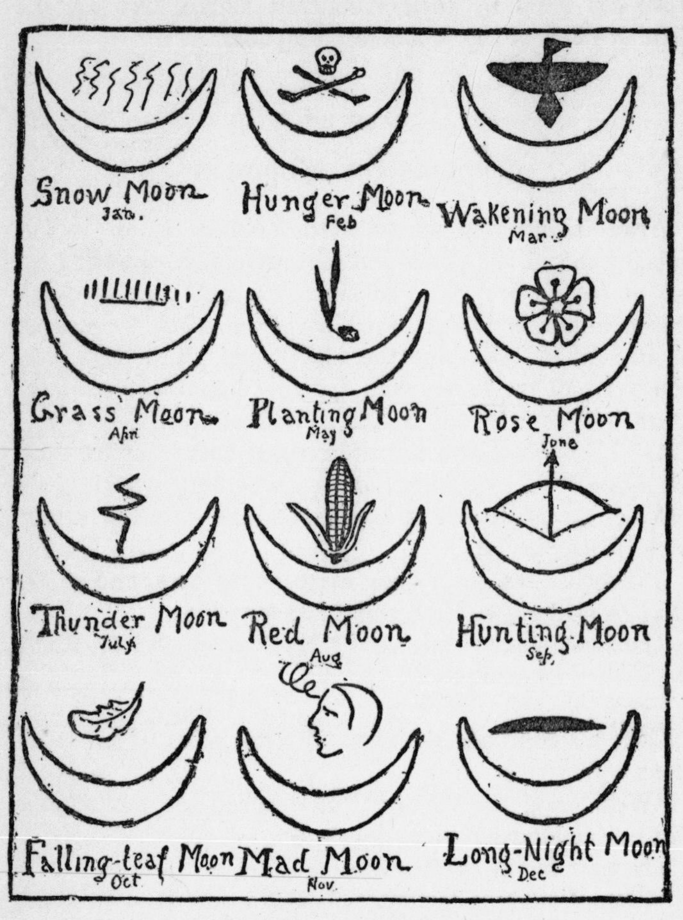

The Woodcraft Kalendar

if we call them by their Woodcraft names, and use the little symbols of the Woodcraft Kalendar.

TALE 107

Climbing the Mountain

AFAR in our dry southwestern country is an Indian village; and in the offing is a high mountain, towering up out of the desert. It is considered a great feat to climb this mountain, so that all the boys of the village were eager to attempt it. One day the Chief said: "Now boys, you you may all go to-day and try to climb the mountain. Start right after breakfast, and go each of you as far as you can. Then when you are tired, come back: but let each one bring me a twig from the place where he turned."

Away they went full of hope, each feeling that he surely could reach the top.

But soon a fat, pudgy boy came slowly back, and in his hand he held out to the Chief a leaf of cactus.

The Chief smiled and said: "My boy, you did not reach the foot of the mountain; you did not even get across the desert."

Later a second boy returned. He carried a twig of sage-brush.

"Well," said the Chief. "You reached the mountain's foot but you did not climb upward."

The next had a cottonwood spray.

"Good," said the Chief; "You got up as far as the springs."

Another came later with some buckthorn. The Chief smiled when he saw it and spoke thus: "You were climbing; you were up to the first slide rock."

Later in the afternoon, one arrived with a cedar spray, and the old man said: "Well done. You went half way up."

An hour afterward, one came with a switch of pine. To him the Chief said: "Good; you went to the third belt; you made three quarters of the climb."

The sun was low when the last returned. He was a tall, splendid boy of noble character. His hand was empty as he approached the Chief, but his countenance was radiant, and he said: "My father, there were no trees where I got to; I saw no twigs, but I saw the Shining Sea."

Now the old man's face glowed too, as he said aloud and almost sang: "I knew it. When I looked on your face, I knew it. You have been to the top. You need no twigs for token. It is written in your eyes, and rings in your voice. My boy, you have felt the uplift, you have seen the glory of the mountain."

Oh Ye Woodcrafters, keep this in mind, then: the badges that we offer for attainment, are not "*prizes*"; prizes are things of value taken by violence from their rightful owners. These are merely tokens of what you have done, of where you have been. They are mere twigs from the trail to show how far you got in climbing the mountain.

THE OMAHA TRIBAL PRAYER.

Harmonized by Prof. J. C. Fillmore.

(By permission from Alice C. Fletcher's "Indian Story and Song.")

Translation:

Father a needy one stands before thee;
I that sing am he.

This old Indian prayer is sung by the Council standing in a great circle about the fire with feet close together, hands and faces uplifted, for it is addressed to the Great Spirit. At the final bars the hands and faces are lowered to the fire.